OCT 14 '81	DATE DUE		
FEB 22 '83			
NOV 5 '84			
FEB 2 8 1986			
OCT 1 4 1986			
NOV 1 4 '89			
MAR 1 5 2012			
DEC 0 6 2012			

Oceanographic Institutions

ALSO BY PETER R. LIMBURG

Chickens, Chickens, Chickens

Oceanographic Institutions

Science studies the sea

PETER R. LIMBURG

ELSEVIER / NELSON BOOKS
New York

Library of Congress Cataloging in Publication Data

Limburg, Peter R
Oceanographic institutions.
Bibliography: p. 252
Includes index.
1. Oceanographic research—United States. 2. Oceanography—Study and teaching (Higher)—United States.
I. Title.
GC58.L55 551.4'6'0072073 78-12214
ISBN 0-525-66505-1

Published in the United States by Elsevier/Nelson Books, a division of Elsevier-Dutton Publishing Company, Inc., New York. Published simultaneously in Don Mills, Ontario, by Thomas Nelson and Sons (Canada) Limited.

Printed in the U.S.A. First Edition
10 9 8 7 6 5 4 3 2 1

TO MY DAUGHTER KARIN
WHOSE INTEREST IN OCEANOGRAPHY SPARKED MY OWN

Acknowledgments

I would like to thank the following persons, without whose generous assistance in granting me interviews, supplying material, or critically reading the pertinent portions of my manuscript this book would never have been completed:

Donald H. Rosenberg, University of Alaska

C. E. Murray, APR, Bedford Institute of Oceanography, Nova Scotia

Dr. G. L. Pickard, University of British Columbia

Mr. Campbell, Dr. Edward F. Chiburis, Dr. Peter Dehlinger, and Dr. William F. Fitzgerald, Marine Sciences Institute of the University of Connecticut

Barbara Goodman, Dalhousie University, Nova Scotia

Dr. Paul R. Austin, Dr. Ellis Bolton, Dr. William S. Gaither, Dr. Billy Glass, Dr. Anton L. Inderbitzen, Kathi Jensen, Dr. Paul Jensen, and Dr. Kent S. Price, College of Marine Studies of the University of Delaware

Dr. S. Körner, Deutsches Hydrographisches Institut, West Germany

Dr. Joseph Bonaventura, Dr. John S. Costlow, Timothy Cowles, Dr. William Kirby-Smith, and Patricia Tester, Duke University Marine Laboratory

Tom Leahy, University of Florida

Jean-Claude Mourlon, scientific attaché, Embassy of France to the United States

Dr. Peter Lundberg, University of Göteborg, Sweden

Peter Anderson, Environmental Protection Agency

Dr. Armin Lindquist and Dr. Bengt Sjöberg, Institute of Marine Research, Sweden

D. W. Privett, Institute of Oceanographic Sciences, United Kingdom

Dr. J. Ulrich, University of Kiel, West Germany

Dr. Jarl-Ove Strömberg, Kristinebergs Biologiska Station, Sweden

Dr. Allan W. H. Bé, Adele Caldara,* David Cooke, Dr. Bruce C. Heezen, Dr. Kenneth L. Hunkins, David Roach, and Charles C. Windisch, Lamont-Doherty Geological Observatory

Sally Kuzenski, University of Louisiana

Dr. James D. Ebert, Jane Fessenden, and Dr. George M. Woodwell, Marine Biological Library

Nena McKnight, Marine Technology Society Journal

A. R. Margetts, Ministry of Agriculture, Fisheries, and Food, United Kingdom

Dr. Alphonse F. Chestnut, Institute of Marine Sciences of the University of North Carolina

Dr. F. G. Walton Smith, International Oceanographic Foundation

Captain Jean Alinat and Jacqueline Carpine-Lancre, Musée Océanographique, Monaco

Christopher du Pont Roosevelt, Oceanic Society

Dr. Harris B. Stewart, Jr., Atlantic Oceanographic and Meteorological Laboratory, NOAA

Dr. Ford A. Cross and John Reintjes, Beaufort Laboratory, NOAA

* no longer with institution

Dr. Robert Abel and Dr. Tom Murray, National Sea Grant

Richard Stevens, Office of Naval Research

Dr. Wayne V. Burt and Dr. James E. McCauley, School of Oceanography, Oregon State University

Alina Froelich, Dr. Dana R. Kester, Dr. John A. Knauss, Virginia Lee, Guy Marchessault, Dr. Theodore A. Napora, Dr. David M. Pratt, Dr. Saul B. Saila, Sergio Signorini, Prentice K. Stout, and Dr. Elijah Swift V, Graduate School of Oceanography of the University of Rhode Island

Alan Baldridge, Eric Barron, James Gibbons, Dr. José A. Honnorez, Stuart McCormick, Dr. Frank J. Millero, Dr. Arthur A. Myrberg, Dr. Henry Perkins, Dr. Jon C. Staiger, and Dr. Warren J. Wisby, Rosenstiel School of Marine and Atmospheric Science of the University of Miami

Nelson Fuller, Betty Shor, and Carl Sisskind (DSDP representative), Scripps Institution of Oceanography

Shirley Hudgins, Institute for Marine Studies, University of Southern California

Dr. Ivar W. Duedall, Dr. J. L. McHugh, Dr. Harold B. O'Connors, Jr., Dr. J. R. Schubel, Dr. Peter K. Weyl, and Dr. Charles F. Wurster, Marine Sciences Research Center of the State University of New York, Stony Brook

Robert Bunting, Texas A & M University

Dr. John L. Dupuy, Ann Greer, Dr. William J. Hargis, Jr., Robert J. Huggett, Dr. Maurice P. Lynch, and Dr. John M. Zeigler, Virginia Institute of Marine Science

Patricia Peyton and Dr. Alyn C. Duxbury, University of Washington

Dr. Melbourne G. Briscoe, Dr. James R. Heirtzler, Tom Losordo, Dr. Mary Sears, Dr. Derek W. Spencer, Dr. Thomas R. Stetson (UNOLS representative), Dr. John M. Teal, William A. Watkins, and Dr. Ferris Webster, Woods Hole Oceanographic Institution

Special thanks to Brian E. Gorman, assistant public affairs officer, National Sea Grant Program, and Richard C. Vetter, executive secretary, Ocean Sciences Board, National Academy of Sciences, for the herculean task of reading my manuscript and for their sound advice, most of which I took; and to Vicky Cullen of Woods Hole Oceanographic Institution, Christi Duerr of the University of Rhode Island, James A. Lanier, III, Virginia Institute of Marine Science, Anne Nixon of Lamont–Doherty Geological Observatory, and Jean Yehle of the Rosenstiel School of Marine and Atmospheric Science, who did everything they could to make my visits to their institutions a success.

Table of Contents

Oceanographic Institutions

About This Book

This book does not attempt to tell everything about oceanographic institutions. To do so would require many hundreds of pages, and the final result would be a catalog, not a book. Instead, it attempts to give a general introduction to the world of oceanographic institutions and their work, touching on the highlights. The institutions that this book covers will have to stand as representatives of the many others that have been omitted.

I have covered institutions large and small, in the United States and abroad, all of them acknowledged as leaders in one field or another of oceanographic research. When possible, I visited them personally in order to get a firsthand impression. When dealing with administrators at a distance, it was not always easy to get the needed information, and some leading oceanographic institutions have been omitted because it was impossible to obtain information from them.

However, most of the scientists, students, technicians, department heads, and public-information people with whom I dealt were extremely helpful, and most had an interesting story to tell. Researching this book was a fascinating experience, and it opened a new world to me. I hope my readers will find it just as interesting and that it will also impart some useful information to those who are thinking of making a career in one or another of the fields of marine science.

Some scientists draw a strict line between "oceanography" and "marine science." By their definition, oceanography is the study of systems and their interactions in the ocean. As one scientist explained it, the study of the life cycle of a flounder in itself is not oceanography. The study of the same flounder in relation to its total environment, including the temperature and chemical composition of the water, the nature of the sea bottom, the flounder's prey and predators and all the other living organisms that share the water with it, is oceanography.

Marine science is a much broader term, covering oceanography and many other aspects of research into the sea. All oceanographers are marine scientists, but not all marine scientists are oceanographers.

Yet it is often hard for an outsider to distinguish between the two. The broad field of marine science and engineering is what most laymen mean when they speak of oceanography. And in practice the differences tend to blur.

During the course of researching this book, I visited a number of institutions and corresponded with others. Some called themselves "oceanographic" and others "marine science." At both, I found a number of scientists doing the same kinds of work. At oceanography schools I found scientists investigating the behavior of a single species of marine animal; at marine-science schools I met people who insisted that they were not oceanographers, yet still were investigating the effects of man-made pollutants on whole ecosystems.

I hope, therefore, that I will be forgiven if I sometimes use the two terms interchangeably.

1

What Is Oceanography?

Gaily colored fish glide past the cameras as the divers explore the teeming life of a tropical coral reef. Here a giant clam exposes its colorful mantle; there a moray eel protrudes its drab, snaky head from the cranny in the coral where it makes its lair, powerful jaws ready to grapple with any antagonist. Now the camera pans in for a close-up of the smaller beings that inhabit the reef: sea anemones with their waving, flowerlike tentacles, sea urchins bristling with venomous spines, scuttling crabs, brightly striped snapping shrimps, camouflaged fish that blend so perfectly with their background that they are invisible until they move. Their black wet suits gleaming dully in the glow of the floodlights, Captain Cousteau and his diving companions move off with powerful strokes of their swim fins to explore the fantastically shaped coral formations. A few yards away, the face of the reef plunges clifflike into the blackness of the depths. The only sound in this silent world is the hoarse bubbling of the scuba apparatus. Above the divers waits the sleek research vessel *Calypso,* which has carried Cousteau and his team on so many fascinating explorations of the sea.

In other TV specials, the Cousteau team swims beside a sperm whale in the dim, blue light fifty feet below the surface, dwarfed by the animal's bulk. Sharks circle slowly, menacingly, as the *Calypso*'s scientists film a record of shark behavior from the safety of a steel-barred cage suspended beneath the surface. In a happier mood, the divers perform a graceful underwater ballet with friendly, curious sea lions amid the golden-brown stems of giant kelp.

To millions of people who have followed Cousteau vicariously on his dramatic and fascinating adventures via books and TV specials, oceanography is summed up in the presentations of this charismatic French explorer of the undersea world. In actuality, Cousteau's work represents only one small and specialized aspect of it. For oceanography is the study of the ocean in *all* its aspects.

Oceanography, therefore, is not a single science, but rather the sum of many sciences, all of which contribute to man's understanding of the ocean: physics, chemistry, biology, geology, meteorology, mathematics, and their subdivisions. Oceanography, in return, contributes new knowledge to these disciplines. To geology, for example, oceanography has contributed the concept of plate tectonics, one of the most important ideas of the century. Plate tectonics, and the associated concept of seafloor spreading, explain how the world's continents came to be the way they are and gives valuable insights into the nature of earthquakes and volcanic activity—insights that may help us predict quakes and eruptions with greater accuracy and save many lives.

The study of ocean sediments and their fossils reveals much about the Earth's climate in past ages, while the ocean's role in influencing today's and tomorrow's weather has long been known. And more is constantly being learned about the interaction of sea and atmosphere.

To biology, oceanographic research has contributed new knowledge of the complex interrelationships among living organisms, such as the members of a coral-reef community; the special adaptations that enable fishes to survive in the absolute dark and freezing cold of the abyss; and the nature of the mysterious "deep scattering layer" that distorts echo-sounding readings.

These examples are just a few, taken at random, of the thousands of ways oceanography has increased our knowledge of the world in general.

The study of oceanography today is divided into four major fields. *Physical oceanography* deals with such things as the temperature and density of seawater at varying depths; the tides, currents, and waves; the way that seawater transmits light and sound. *Meteorological oceanography,* the study of the interactions of sea and atmosphere, is usually considered a branch of physical oceanography.

Chemical oceanography is concerned with the chemistry of the ocean in all its ramifications—not only the chemical composition of seawater, but also such questions as these: Where do pollutants come from? What happens to oil and other pollutants that are spilled into the sea? How long do radioactive particles stay in circulation? How are mineral deposits formed on the seabed? How much dissolved oxygen is contained in a sample of seawater from a given location, and why? Increasingly, chemical oceanographers are becoming involved in such problems as how chemical compounds move through the food chain—nutrients as well as pollutants. They are also concerned with what happens to pollutants when they are taken up by living organisms. Where do they go? Which plants and animals tend to absorb them most readily? Are they concentrated in a particular part of the body tissues? How do they react and interact in living tissues? Are they metabolized into harmless forms? How long does it take for man-made poisons like DDT to break down? Under what conditions do they break down most rapidly?

Geological and geophysical oceanography deal with the sediments and the underlying rocks of the ocean floor and with its hills, valleys, mountains, basins, and canyons. Using specialized tools, such as piston corers and bottom dredges, the geological oceanographers discover what is on or under the ocean floor. The geophysicists explain why it is there. An important part of geological oceanographers' work is locating likely sites for petroleum and other mineral deposits. And, by studying the fossils in ocean sediments and sedimentary rocks, geological oceanographers bring to light buried chapters of the Earth's history, including what the climate was like in past geological periods. Mapping the ocean floor is also part of geological oceanography.

Geophysicists, examining the ocean ridges, rifts, and trenches, learn about the way the continents were formed and about the underlying causes of earthquakes and volcanic eruptions. In some oceanographic institutions, geological and geophysical oceanography are combined in the same department; in others, they are given separate departments.

Biological oceanography is the branch of oceanography with which the public is most familiar. It takes in everything from the largest whales to the tiniest one-celled microorganisms.

A biological oceanographer may specialize in the study of a single organism, such as a deep-sea starfish, but his work is principally concerned with ecological systems. In fact, this is what makes biological oceanography different from marine biology. The marine biologist studies a fish, a clam, or a seaweed for itself. The biological oceanographer studies it as part of a system. Studying a scallop by itself—its anatomy, its metabolism, its genetic makeup—is marine biology. Studying that same scallop as part of a system that includes other scallops, starfish, predatory snails, algae, the sea bottom, the water, and hundreds of other living organisms that prey on the scallop, serve as food for it, or compete with it for food and living space, is biological oceanography.

One of the major concerns of biological oceanographers is the management of fishery resources. This involves studying the breeding and feeding habits and the growth rates of fishes, so that the people in charge of regulating the fisheries will know how many fish can safely be harvested. Overfishing can bring huge catches for a year or two, but in the long run, with fewer young fish produced each year, it will reduce the numbers of the species so much that there won't be enough to be worth catching.

Another major problem that biological oceanographers deal with is pollution and its effects on the marine environment. This has innumerable ramifications: How do oil spills affect the behavior of crabs and lobsters? Do they disturb these edible crustaceans' nervous systems so that they cannot locate food or do not breed? How are PCBs* passed up through the food chain? How long do they last before breaking down? What are their effects on the organisms that take them in? Biological oceanographers are also helping to develop better methods of aquaculture to raise fish, shellfish, and commercially useful seaweeds.

In addition, they study the effects on the environment of such man-made changes as building a nuclear power plant by the shore, dumping dredging spoil in a bay, and allowing the runoff of farm and lawn fertilizers to drain into the sea.

Each branch of oceanography is closely tied to the others. For example, biological oceanographers need to know enough physical oceanography to understand the upwelling currents that bring nutrient-rich water to the surface. They need to know enough chemical oceanography to understand how the minerals carried by the upwelling water fertilize an abundant crop of plankton, which in turn supports a dense population of fish.

The chemical oceanographer needs physics to explain how

---

* PCBs (short for polychlorinated biphenyls) are a class of man-made substances that are used in electrical transformers, plastics, and a host of other products. They are highly resistant to heat and fire, chemically stable, electrically conductive, and poisonous. They have been manufactured since the 1920's, but their poisonous effects were not discovered until 1968.

bodies of ocean water of different salt and mineral contents mix. He must know enough biology to understand how living organisms affect the chemistry of seawater: for instance, how clams take dissolved calcium and carbon dioxide from seawater to build their shells, making the water much more acid; how dead, decaying organisms rob the water of oxygen; and how one-celled green plants add oxygen. He needs geology to understand how underwater volcanoes add minerals to seawater, and how rivers bring down still other chemicals from the land.

A physical oceanographer needs his knowledge of biology to understand that water is sometimes cloudy because of multitudes of one-celled organisms that interfere with the passage of light, or how the bladders of midwater fish reflect sound waves and give false depth readings. Chemistry tells him how the salinity of water affects its density and thus its ability to conduct sound.

A geological oceanographer needs chemistry to analyze the makeup of rocks and sediments and physics to date them by means of radioactive isotopes or paleomagnetism. Physics also tells him how wind and water currents have transported the sediments he is studying. Biology gives him the ability to date sediments and rocks by the fossils he finds in them. Some ocean rocks, such as corals, are formed by living organisms. Biology tells the geological oceanographer under what conditions such rocks are formed—and how they are torn down by other living organisms, such as burrowing clams and worms that drill into the coral, crown-of-thorns starfish that crawl over the reefs, digesting coral polyps as they go, and parrot fish that bite off chunks of living coral with their powerful beaks and pass the indigestible residue out as fine, white coral sand.

Not actually a part of oceanography, but using some of the same equipment and techniques, is marine archaeology. Scuba-equipped archaeologists dive down to investigate ancient shipwrecks and sunken cities. One team uncovered a Greek merchant ship that sank in a storm in the fourth century B.C. The wreck still held its load of wine jars, millstones, and almonds. Clay seals on the jars gave clues to the buyers, sellers, and port officials who approved the shipments, which helped historians to trace the ancient Mediterranean trade networks. One side of the ship was still preserved by being buried deep in sediments. This was firsthand evidence of how ancient Greek shipwrights built their vessels. Even the cook's utensils had somehow survived.

Another team explored the ruins of Port Royal, Jamaica, a notorious pirate stronghold that thrived in the late 1600's. English, French, and Dutch freebooters congregated in this wide-open town, selling stolen goods to legitimate merchants and roistering away the profits. On a Sunday morning in 1692 a violent earthquake sank Port Royal beneath the water, where it remained untouched until an archaeological team led by an American named Robert Marx began exploring it in the 1960's.

On the practical side, applied oceanography has hundreds of achievements to its credit. A sampling could include such accomplishments as these:

Mining manganese nodules and other mineral resources from the seafloor.

Developing special seafloor wellhead equipment for offshore oil wells.

Developing undersea habitats where scientists and technicians can spend a month or more beneath the water, conducting scientific research or doing such practical work as checking underwater pipelines.

Designing and building a great variety of submersibles, able to do work ranging from collecting scientific specimens to salvaging sunken airplanes and ships or exploring the ocean depths at levels as great as 12,000 feet.

Finding more efficient ways of raising edible shellfish in captivity.

Inventing systems for luring fish by means of sound waves or a weak electric current.

Finding the safest place to bury radioactive wastes from nuclear power plants.

The ocean has been called Earth's last frontier, and as man's exploding population swarms over virtually all the Earth's usable land surface, this becomes even truer. The ocean, which covers over 70 percent of the world, is the last remaining area that man has not conquered. But this may not hold true for many more years. Improved sonar devices have mapped large areas of the seafloor in relief. Submerged TV cameras, towed from surface vessels, capture on tape a visual record of the oceans and their inhabitants.

Man has even begun to penetrate the ocean depths in person, using specially designed submersible vessels. The task is in many ways comparable to the exploration of outer space, and the environment is in some respects even more hostile. Like the astronauts, aquanauts must be able to operate in isolation, literally cut off from the world, and under conditions where a single mistake may spell death. Like space capsules, research submersibles must be able to stand extreme stresses and pressure differences and pack a great deal of sophisticated equipment into a very limited space. NASA, the government agency that put the first men on the moon, has also been involved in a number of undersea research projects. And a former astronaut, Scott Carpenter, has been a leader in Navy projects to explore our deep frontier.

As man continues to probe the depths, each advance in our knowledge of the ocean and its processes will be an addition to that body of sciences we call oceanography.

2

The Beginnings of Oceanography

Man has probably always been curious about the sea. Why is it salty? Why do the tides rise and fall? Why doesn't the sea overflow during the rainy season and shrink to a puddle in the dry season? What sorts of monsters live in it? Long before the time of Aristotle (fourth century B.C.), Greek philosophers were asking these questions. And doubtless for thousands of years before that, every people that lived on a seacoast had been asking them, too.

Yet man also feared the ocean, with its storms and waves, its tricky currents, its hidden reefs and shoals. In his imagination he peopled its depths with demons and monsters. For these reasons, and also because he had no way of getting more than a few feet below the surface or of remaining under for more than a minute or two, he never explored the sea as he explored the land.

The Greek philosophers speculated ingeniously about the questions mentioned above, and others, but they considered it unworthy of a scholar to make actual observations of the things he was theorizing about. Aristotle, who was an excellent observer himself, remarked in disgust that his philosophical colleagues had produced no theory that the most ordinary man could not have thought of. The scientific study of the ocean really begins with

Aristotle, who was a keen-eyed marine biologist and deserves to rank as one of the fathers of oceanography.

After Aristotle, however, scholars again neglected the sea for centuries, although sailors and fishermen piled up a good amount of information about the shoals, winds, reefs, and currents in the parts of the world they were familiar with. Not until the late seventeenth century did scientists again turn their attention to the ocean. By then some of the basic laws of physics had been worked out, mathematics were flourishing, and chemistry was beginning to emerge from the mysticism of alchemy. Just as important, ships of many nations were plying the high seas, aided by improved instruments for navigation and new navigational tables worked out by scientists.

England took an early lead in the scientific study of the oceans. In the 1680's Isaac Newton, the famed mathematician and astronomer, worked out the basic theory of the tides. Newton's contemporary, Robert Hooke, known for his work on springs, barometers, and microscopes, developed an instrument for gauging depth by means of the water pressure. Robert Boyle, discoverer of the gas laws, investigated the temperature and salinity of ocean water in different parts of the world. Unfortunately, the land-bound Boyle had to depend on sailors and travelers for his data, and sailors were not interested in making careful and regular observations, while cooperative travelers were rare. Boyle was also hampered by the lack of reliable instruments—the thermometer and the hydrometer had only recently been invented and were still full of "bugs."

Another English astronomer who did work in oceanography was Edmond Halley, discoverer of Halley's comet. As a government official, one of Halley's assignments was to make a two-year voyage far south in the Atlantic Ocean to study wind patterns and terrestrial magnetism. So far south did he travel that his ship encountered icebergs from the Antarctic. This trip kept Halley at sea from 1698 to 1700. Soon after his return, he made a survey of the tides and coasts of the English Channel. He also invented an improved diving bell with a continuous air supply. Earlier diving bells could stay down only about half an hour, as their only air was what they had inside when they were sent down, and this was soon used up by the divers. Halley's bell, with air supplied by barrels and hoses, could in theory stay down indefinitely. Although Halley's invention was used only for salvage and harbor work, it was a step forward in man's penetration of the underwater world.

After the great burst of activity in the late 1600's, little oceanographic research was done for almost another century. An Italian nobleman, Count Luigi Marsigli, did some pioneer hydrographic work in the Mediterranean off Marseilles, mapping the bottom and measuring water temperature and salinity. He also noted down his findings on tides, currents, and marine life. However, the scholarly count was forced to cut his research short because of a lack of money, a fate suffered by a number of modern oceanographic researchers.

American oceanography began with Benjamin Franklin's studies of the Gulf Stream. About 1770, when Franklin was deputy postmaster general for Britain's North American colonies, the customs officials in Boston raised a fuss in London over the mail deliveries. They complained that the British packets from Falmouth to New York, which carried the official mail, took two weeks longer than the American merchantmen that sailed from London to Rhode Island. They wished all official mail to be sent to Rhode Island henceforth. Franklin had a hard time understanding this at first, since the packets were not only faster and more lightly loaded than the merchant ships, but also had about two hundred miles less far to sail. But in London he ran into a Nantucket sea captain whom he knew; in fact, they were cousins. His nautical relative told him that the English ships were delayed because they were sailing against a three-mile-an-hour current in the ocean. The New Englanders who captained the merchant ships knew about the current, said the Nantucketer, but the Englishmen who captained the packets thought themselves too wise to be counseled by simple American fishermen.

New England seamen knew the Gulf Stream from their whaling voyages. They knew it as a place to avoid, because whales were rarely seen within it. To Franklin his cousin passed on some tips: The Gulf Stream was blue and warm; the North Atlantic water on either side of it was cold and gray. Fish abounded in the Atlantic; they were hardly ever found in the Gulf Stream.

Franklin asked his New England relative to mark the course of the Gulf Stream on a map, for up to then it had been uncharted. Then, seized by the lust for scientific inquiry, he decided to map it himself on his voyages between America and Europe. He began in 1775, was stopped by the Revolution, and began again in 1785. Though Franklin had only a thermometer to work with, by taking the temperature of the water and the air above it, and by noting the water's color and the fish and floating seaweed that he saw, he was able to make a surprisingly accurate chart of the Gulf Stream's path across the northern Atlantic.

Even before Franklin began to track the Gulf Stream, various European governments were sending out naval expeditions to explore seas and coasts as yet unknown, and to find new opportunities for commerce. One of the greatest of the commanders was Captain James Cook. The son of an English farm laborer, Cook began his career at age twelve as a haberdasher's apprentice. A few years later he was serving as a merchant seaman, rising to the rank of mate. Cook then switched to the Royal Navy as an ordinary seaman and within a few years was promoted to master of a vessel—a very unusual happening in the caste-ridden British navy. Before his death in 1779 in a quarrel with some Hawaiians who had stolen a boat from his ship, Cook had explored the Alaskan coast, circled Antarctica, explored the southern tip of South America, New Zealand, much of Australia, and many of the Pacific islands. His descriptions of exotic peoples, animals, and plants created a sensation in Europe. During his three expeditions he also made valuable hydrographic and astronomical observations. Whalers and sealers were quick to take advantage of Cook's reports of the rich marine life of the southern seas; traders found valuable commodities in the islands which, thanks to Cook's charts, they could reach safely.

Cook's success spurred a flurry of similar expeditions. In the meantime, natural historians were beginning to investigate the plants and animals of Europe's coastal waters, sometimes wading in the shallows, sometimes rowing out in a boat. After 1800, discoveries came at an increasingly faster pace. For example, in 1819 a Swiss-born London chemist named Alexander Marcet proved that seawater from all over the world contains the same dissolved chemical compounds, or salts. Moreover, he found that these dissolved substances are always in the same ratio to each other, even though the saltiness of the water varies. This discovery was especially useful because it enabled a researcher to compute the total salt content of a sample of seawater by measuring just one of the dissolved substances. (Later researchers, with better equipment, found that there are small variations in the ratios of the dissolved substances, but Marcet's basic principle still holds true.) Marcet also found that, unlike fresh water, which expands as it reaches freezing point, salt water contracts until it freezes. This was to be of great importance in plotting the circulation of the deep ocean waters.

An English military officer, James Rennell, who turned to science after being disabled in a clash with religious fanatics in India, made a pioneering study of currents in the Indian and Atlantic oceans. (The study was published in 1832, two years after his death.) About the same time a French physicist named Gaspard de Coriolis explained the laws that govern the motions of wind and water currents, bending them toward the right in the Northern Hemisphere and the left in the Southern Hemisphere. The inertial force that caused this behavior was later named in Coriolis' honor.

Permanent programs of investigation began to take shape in the 1840's, and important discoveries about the ocean came more frequently. In the United States, a young naval lieutenant named Matthew Fontaine Maury began his lifework of collecting data on winds and currents. Within a few years Maury's work began to pay off in the form of navigational charts. Although the routes Maury suggested looked roundabout on the map, they brought seamen to their destinations faster than the old-fashioned straight-line routes. One route on which the saving in time was particularly noticeable was the long voyage from the east coast of the United States to California around Cape Horn. Some vessels saved as much as a month between New York and San Francisco.

Maury also published a whaling chart (1851), but his most ambitious project was to encourage seafaring nations to form an international maritime meteorological conference and exchange information for the benefit of all. A conference, the first of its kind, was held in 1853, and eventually nineteen nations took part in Maury's master plan of publishing abstracts from their ships' logs to increase the general fund of knowledge of winds, currents, and weather at sea.

Maury's services were temporarily lost to his country during the Civil War—Maury, a Virginian, served on the Confederate side and after the war lived in Mexico and England. In 1868 he took advantage of a general amnesty to come home and ended his days as a professor of meteorology at Virginia Military Institute.

Maury also wrote many articles and books. His most popular work, *Physical Geography of the Sea* (1855), was translated into several European languages. Curiously, it was published in England a year before it came out in the United States. Perhaps bureaucratic rivalries delayed its publication in its author's homeland. *Physical Geography of the Sea* still ranks as one of the classics of oceanographic literature, even though many of Maury's theories were later found to be mistaken.

Maury's great rival in American oceanography was Alexander Dallas Bache, a great-grandson of Benjamin Franklin and head of the United States Coastal Survey. Bache had staked out the Gulf Stream as his personal preserve for investigation, whereas Maury claimed it as Navy territory. The rivalry between the two scientists did serve to stimulate the study of the Gulf Stream, and new instruments were devised for taking soundings and water temperatures.

Thermometers had an unfortunate way of being crushed by water pressure at depths below 3,000 feet, even when protected by metal cases. Finally someone hit on the idea of enclosing the thermometers in glass globes. When properly tempered, glass has the property of gaining strength as the pressure on it increases, and the globe is one of the strongest structural shapes. Thus the glass globes were able to protect the fragile thermometer tubes.

In 1848 one of Bache's research vessels turned over some samples of sediment to a professor at West Point. When the professor examined them under his microscope, he discovered that they were largely made up of the tiny, delicate shells of microorganisms called *foraminifera*. He realized that these organisms lived in the surface layers of the sea and sank to the bottom when they died. Today fossil forams, as they are called for short, are indispensable for the study of geology and paleoclimatology (the study of the climate of past ages.)

Meanwhile, the great voyages of exploration were still going on. From 1838 to 1842 Charles Wilkes, an American naval officer, sailed between 80,000 and 90,000 miles exploring Antarctica, New Zealand, Southern Australia, the South Pacific islands, and the west coast of North America. Since the pack ice was less than usual in 1839–40, Wilkes could get close enough to the Antarctic continent to catch frequent glimpses of land (Cook had never gotten that close). Almost at the same time (1839–1843), the British scientist Sir James Clark Ross explored Antarctica and the surrounding waters. Both men claimed to have discovered the southernmost continent, but no one went to war over the ownership of the frozen, inaccessible expanse of ice and barren rock.

An unexpected factor in the growth of oceanography was the development of the telegraph in the 1830's and 1840's. As the network of overland telegraph lines grew in America and in Europe, foresighted businessmen began to think of running telegraph cables underwater. Samuel F. B. Morse led off with a successful cable under New York Harbor in 1842. In 1850 an English businessman named John Brett laid a cable across the English Channel. Other lines followed; from Nova Scotia to Newfoundland; in the Mediterranean; in the North Sea. It seemed plain that a transatlantic cable was the next step. Indeed, as early as 1852, Maury published a chart of a proposed telegraph route, based on U.S. Navy soundings. Unfortunately, his soundings were taken so far apart that they missed many important features of bottom topography. For example, Maury believed the Mid-Atlantic Ridge, now known to be extremely rugged and cleft with a deep, 30-mile-wide canyon, to be a smooth, level plateau, which seemed, as he put it, "to have been placed there for the purpose of holding the wires of a submarine telegraph." He actually named this supposed underwater platform the Telegraphic Plateau.

The impetus—and the money—for the cable came from a wealthy American businessman, Cyrus Field, and from the Englishman Brett. Scientific and technical expertise were supplied by a young English engineer, Charles Bright, and a Scottish physicist named William Thomson, later to become famous as Lord Kelvin, author of the second law of thermodynamics. Able and gifted as these men were, they still needed to know more about the seafloor along the proposed cable route, from Newfoundland to the southwest corner of Ireland. Maury's men had taken only thirty soundings along a 2,000-mile stretch of seafloor, and much more closely spaced depth measurements were needed. Was the bottom rough or smooth? Rocky, sandy, or silty? Were there rises and deeps?

In 1856 the American and British governments detailed naval ships to the job of taking soundings. The next summer the actual work of laying the cable began. We have room here for only a few of the highlights of the story. The two governments each lent their largest, most modern steam-powered warships for the task; they fought storms and broken cables until two years later the transatlantic telegraph link was completed. Queen Victoria and President Buchanan exchanged messages of congratulation by wire. Field and his associates became instant heroes on both sides of the Atlantic; Bright was knighted for his services. But a few weeks later the cable went dead, burned out by too high a voltage.

Field was nearly wiped out financially by this disaster, and the Civil War soon put a stop to any operations. But he bounced back in 1865, raised new funds, and chartered the *Great Eastern,* the world's largest ship, for his cable-laying vessel. Once more mishaps prolonged the task, but on July 27, 1866, the job was completed. As a side benefit to oceanography, the cable project contributed improved machinery for paying out and hauling in heavy cables, and new tools and techniques for recovering objects from the bottom. (The second cable, which broke in 1865 some 1,200 miles out from land, was hooked and lost again twenty-nine times before finally being secured.)

While Maury and others had been mapping the seafloor and tracing currents, the biologists had been busy, too. Wilkes and Ross both had naturalists among their civilian scientist corps, and they eagerly studied the fish and other organisms captured by their nets. One rare specimen, a dragonlike little fish with oddly shaped fins, was discovered frozen in a mass of ice that had formed on the ship's bow. The ship's naturalist sketched it hastily, then put it aside to thaw out for a detailed examination. Unfortunately for science, the ship's cat got there first and devoured the specimen. Not until sixty years later was another fish of that species seen, by a Belgian expedition to Antarctica.

Ross also encouraged his scientists to dredge the bottom for life forms whenever the ship neared land. Among other things, they used a device invented by Ross's uncle, Sir John Ross, on an expedition to Baffin Bay twenty years earlier. The device, called a "deep-sea clamm," was an early version of today's clamshell dredges. Effective down to nearly 6,000 feet, it brought up live worms from the Arctic seafloor and worms and shellfish from the Antarctic bottom, from depths as great as 2,400 feet. Here was conclusive proof that life existed in the ocean depths.

Despite this evidence, most scientists held to the belief that life could not exist below about 300 fathoms (1,800 feet). The strongest supporter of this theory was, curiously enough, a brilliant English biologist named Edward Forbes, who ranks with Matthew Maury as one of the fathers of oceanography. Early in the nineteenth century, many scientists believed that the ocean depths were filled with a stagnant, airless layer of very cold water where no life could exist for lack of oxygen. Forbes had dredged the bottom of the sea off Britain and in the Aegean. In both cases he had gotten very scanty hauls of animals from depths of about 1,400 feet and rich hauls from shallow waters. On the basis of these insufficient results, he announced in 1841 that the waters below 1,800 feet were an "azoic" (lifeless) zone. Animals that had been captured by dredges in deeper waters, he explained, must have been scooped in by accident as the dredge was pulled up.

Not until 1860 did the azoic-zone theory receive its death blow, and again a submarine telegraph cable was responsible. A cable had been laid in more than 6,000 feet of water near the island of Sardinia. When it failed three years later and was hauled up for repair, it was found to have sponges and other sedentary sea animals growing on it—in some cases, growing entirely around it! There was no way in which these animals could have been picked up by the cable as it was hauled to the surface—even the most hardened supporters of the azoic theory had to admit it. A section of the animal-encrusted cable was exhibited at the prestigious French Academy of Sciences, which officially ratified the existence of life in the depths, at least as far as scientists were concerned.

Even before this, some naturalists had been pushing the boundary of the "azoic zone" deeper and deeper. One was a Norwegian scientist named P. C. Asbjörnsen, who was also a noted collector of folklore. Asbjörnsen dredged up some large, luminous starfish from the deep waters off Norway, at about 1,800 feet. Another pioneering Norwegian marine biologist was Michael Sars, who in the 1860's dredged living animals from depths of one to two miles. Some of these did not look at all like animals, but rather like underwater flowers. These were the crinoids, or sea lilies, actually members of the same phylum as starfish, sea urchins, and sea cucumbers. More interesting yet, Sars's deep-sea crinoids looked much more like fossil types than the familiar crinoids that grew in shallow water. The fossils that they resembled had been found in deposits from the Cretaceous period, about 100 million years ago. Here indeed were "living fossils" to back up the evolutionary theories of Charles Darwin.

Once the azoic-zone theory had been disproved, many scientists looked eagerly to the deep waters as a living museum of ancient forms of life that had died out eons ago elsewhere, but lived on in the frigid, ever dark isolation of the depths. As it later turned out, the scientists' hopes were disappointed. Most of the deep-dwellers are modern organisms. Only now and then does a true "living fossil" turn up, such as the celebrated coelacanth or the tiny pink-and-blue *Neopilina,* which seems to be a link between worms and mollusks.

The search for living fossils in the depths led to an amusing incident or a classic scientific blooper, depending on your viewpoint. In 1868 Thomas Huxley, a leading British scientist and Darwin's chief defender, picked up a specimen flask that had been lying neglected in his laboratory for eleven years. The flask contained a sample of mud from the Telegraphic Plateau in the North Atlantic that had been pickled in alcohol to preserve it. To his astonishment, Huxley noticed a thin layer of a strange, jellylike substance lying on top of the mud. In the jelly, which resembled mucus, were tiny granules. Huxley examined a dab of the jelly under his microscope and saw the granules slowly shift position, like the granules in protoplasm. He decided that this must be an exceedingly primitive organism, and he named it *Bathybius haeckelii.* (*Bathybius,* meaning "deep life," is from the Greek, and the *haeckelii* is in honor of the German naturalist Ernst Haeckel.)

Haeckel himself soon had a chance to examine a sample of Huxley's jelly, and his enthusiastic imagination ran wild. This jellylike substance, Haeckel postulated, was a tiny portion of a vast sheet of living substance that carpeted the ocean floor, feeding on organic detritus in the ooze. Higher organisms, in turn, fed on *Bathybius*. Moreover, theorized Haeckel, *Bathybius* must be the "primeval slime" (*Urschleim* in German) from which all other forms of life were descended.

Haeckel's theory caused great excitement among the scientific community—only to be dashed a few years later when a chemist on the *Challenger* expedition discovered that *Bathybius* was simply a chemical precipitate formed by mixing seawater and alcohol!

The *Challenger* expedition (December 1872 to May 1876) was one of the great oceanographic voyages of all time. During the forty-one months it lasted, it covered 68,890 miles, crossed the equator six times, collected data in every one of the world's oceans except the Arctic, and made soundings at 362 stations, zigzagging back and forth across each ocean several times. Although it was a British enterprise paid for by British taxpayers, as some newspapers huffily pointed out, the data were made available to scientists of all nations, an international team was hired to write them up, and the youngest scientist on the expedition, twenty-five-year-old Rudolf von Willemoes-Suhm, was a German. Thus the *Challenger* expedition was a forerunner of today's international cooperation among oceanographic scientists.

H.M.S. *Challenger,* the ship that gave its name to the expedition, was a speedy naval corvette slightly adapted for scientific operations. Its 226-foot wooden hull held three masts plus a 1,234-horsepower steam engine and twin 9-horsepower donkey engines to power the winch. Because there was little space for storing coal, the powerful engine was seldom used, and most of the voyage was made under sail. The donkey engines, as it turned out, were not always equal to the task of hauling up a heavily loaded dredge and had to be helped by an unenthusiastic gang of sailors.

Seven scientists, assisted by some 230 naval officers and sailors, somehow found space for themselves and their bulky collecting gear on board. Four naturalists, a chemist, an artist, and a photographer made up the civilian scientific corps. The navy men took care of all magnetic and meteorological observations in addition to carrying out the soundings and dredgings. Dredging was a chore particularly dreaded by the officers, who had to stand watch for ten to twelve hours while the heavy iron dredge was dragged slowly across the sea bottom, scooping up mud, rocks, and such forms of bottom life as starfish, sea urchins, and sea cucumbers, which could not even be eaten after the scientists logged them in. Sounding was not nearly as tedious, although it took about an hour and a quarter for the lead to reach bottom in the deepest soundings (around 26,000 feet) and even longer to reel it up again.

The playful young naturalist Willemoes-Suhm (he died of erysipelas on the voyage) trained a parrot to squawk "What, two thousand fathoms and no bottom! Ah, Dr. Carpenter, F.R.S.!" (Carpenter, a noted physiologist and a Fellow of the Royal Society, was the chief promoter of the *Challenger* expedition. He turned down the chance to head it on the grounds that he was too old—he was fifty-nine at the time.)

The drudgery paid off. When the *Challenger* returned to Britain, it brought with it over 13,000 different kinds of animals and plants, which yielded over 700 new genera and 4,000 new species. The *Challenger*'s scientific cargo also included 1,441 water samples and hundreds of samples of seafloor sediments and rocks. It took nineteen years to publish all the reports on the *Challenger*'s findings, and the cost of preparing and publishing the reports was almost as much as that of the whole lengthy voyage.

Far from answering all the questions about the sea, the *Challenger*'s voluminous discoveries opened up more. The next decade saw oceanographic expeditions from the United States, Germany, Norway, Russia, Italy, and France, plus several more from Britain.

In the 1880's Prince Albert of Monaco (1848–1922) began his oceanographic researches. Born to riches and royalty, this remarkable man became a respected marine scientist, pioneer conservationist, and anthropologist. He was also a passionate hunter. Like Theodore Roosevelt, he loved nature and outdoor life, but he lacked T.R.'s childish enthusiasm for war. In fact, in later life he was an outspoken antimilitarist.

Packed off at the age of seventeen to the Spanish navy by his father, Albert learned self-discipline and seamanship, and began his lifelong interest in the sea in all its aspects. Science was not part of the training of royalty in those days, but after service in the navies of Spain and France, Albert taught himself science with the help of a professor at the Sorbonne. His work eventually earned him membership in the French Academy of Science, where he inherited the seat of the great British physicist Lord Kelvin.

His first scientific voyage was in 1885; the vessel was his yacht *Hirondelle* (French for "swallow"), which he had made over into a floating laboratory. For thirty years Prince Albert spent three to four months each year at sea, and a small crew of scientists always accompanied him. He also took along an artist to record the colors of the marine organisms he caught before they faded in death or in the pickling jar.

On his first three voyages the prince released hundreds of floats to chart the flow of the Gulf Stream. But his true interest was marine biology, in particular the animals of the ocean depths, then virtually unknown to science. Prince Albert wondered why so few types of animals had been caught by the nets and dredges of earlier scientists; then he realized that all but the slowest and feeblest were able to get out of the way of the capture devices. Instead, he designed special large fish traps with smaller traps inside, where the lesser creatures could hide from their larger fellows and escape being devoured by them. The traps were sent down and left overnight, each one marked with a flag buoy so that it could be found again the next day. Chunks of fish were hung inside as bait to attract the always-hungry dwellers of the deep. In this way hundreds of previously unknown species of fish, crustaceans, and other kinds of animals were taken.

The prince also experimented with an electrically illuminated trap as early as 1888. Apparently electrical equipment was not reliable for such work, for he later switched to tubes filled with phosphorescent chemicals to attract curious animals. He also devised a mid-depth net that would open and close automatically. In this way the net would take only the animals found at the desired depth. It would not scoop up any outsiders on the way down or the way up. This invention was of great value in ascertaining the depth range at which each species lived.

At times, Albert used extremely unconventional methods to capture specimens. On a cruise to the Azores, he watched native whalemen hunt a sperm whale. From his yacht he observed that the dying whale vomited up an immense mass of squids and octopus. Hastily collecting as many as he could, Albert and his zoological expert found that the cephalopods belonged to entirely new species—deep-water types that could not be caught by man-made devices. After this experience, Albert occasionally used whales as specimen catchers.

A whaleboat would be lowered from the deck of the yacht, and Albert, who liked to do things for himself, manned the harpoon gun. The whale, sacrificed in the interests of science, was measured, dissected, examined, and recorded with meticulous care in the prince's notebooks. It should be said that Prince Albert killed only a few whales, that he regretted their deaths, and that as far back as the 1890's he was appalled at the wholesale slaughter of whales that "feeble governments" permitted.

In addition to his biological researches, Prince Albert took hundreds of soundings, temperature measurements, and samples of water and seafloor sediments. On several voyages he also probed the upper atmosphere with kites and balloons.

The *Hirondelle*, entirely sail-powered, proved unequal to the delicate work of deep-sea sounding, during which the sounding line must be kept vertical to get an accurate measure. This, as you can imagine, is an almost impossible task for a sailing vessel. And its hand-powered winch was not efficient at dredging. Prince Albert once calculated that to take a sounding at a depth of 2,400 meters (about 7,900 feet) and then to dredge the area required 85,000 turns of the crank by his exhausted crewmen. So the *Hirondelle* was replaced by a series of progressively larger and more powerful steam yachts.

It was on one of these yachts, the *Princesse Alice II*, that Prince Albert's guests, Drs. Paul Portier and Charles Richet, did the first experiments in anaphylaxis, using toxins from Portuguese men-of-war fished up by the crew. These experiments eventually led to a Nobel Prize in physiology for Richet. Anaphylaxis is the process by which an organism becomes hypersensitive to a poison after being exposed to it for the first time. Some people, for example, become extremely sensitive to bee stings after being stung once. If they are stung again, they may be so severely affected that they die unless rushed to a hospital for treatment. The treatment used today was developed as a result of the work of Richet and Portier with a primitive marine animal related to the jellyfishes.

Albert's contributions to marine science did not end there, for he also founded the great Musée Océanographique in Monaco and a companion institute in Paris where free courses are offered to university students from all countries.

Beginning in the mid-1860's, Scandinavian scientists became involved in fisheries studies. This led them to study the currents that carry fish larvae and the plankton that support the whole web of fish life. It also led them into pioneering studies of meteorology, since they found they had to learn how winds affect ocean currents, and into studies of the chemical content of seawater, which controls its productivity in terms of fish food. By the end of the century, Sweden, Norway, and Denmark were in the forefront of oceanographic research.

As an outgrowth of the need to study fisheries problems, the International Council for the Exploration of the Sea was founded in 1902, under the auspices of the King of Sweden. The original members of ICES were Sweden, Norway, Denmark, Britain, Finland, Russia, Germany, and the Netherlands, all nations with a big stake in the fish of the North Sea and the North Atlantic. Under ICES, which is still an important, functioning organization, the oceans were studied for the first time as an undivided system.

In 1905 the Scripps Institution of Oceanography was founded; in 1910 the Musée Océanographique in Monaco was opened; in 1912 a German meteorologist and geophysicist named Alfred Wegener proposed the startling theory of continental drift. Work was progressing fast on many oceanographic fronts when World War I broke out and stopped virtually all research.

3

Oceanography from World War I to the Present

Although most scientifically advanced nations were either involved in the fighting of World War I or afraid to send research vessels to sea, the war actually hastened the development of some valuable scientific tools, not the least of which was sonar.

The story of sonar—one of the oceanographer's most valuable tools today—actually dates back to the sinking of the luxury liner *Titanic* by an iceberg in 1912. A few people had been working on ways to transmit sound signals underwater a decade earlier, but it took a major disaster to get things moving. Inventors in the United States, England, and Switzerland were soon at work on sonic iceberg detectors that would give ships warning of bergs even in impenetrable fog or pitch-dark. One inventor, a former Edison researcher named Reginald Fessenden, had his device ready for testing in April 1914, before the war broke out.

Fessenden's device was simple and effective. An oscillator, something like an oversized electric door buzzer, was lowered into the water over the ship's side, and sent out sound waves in all directions. A pair of hydrophones—waterproof microphones mounted below the ship's waterline—picked up the echoes as they bounced back from solid surfaces such as an iceberg or the seafloor. Fessenden himself realized that his invention could be used for taking speedy depth soundings, although that was not his original purpose. Tested on a Coast Guard cutter in the North Atlantic, the sonic device performed brilliantly, picking up the echoes from an iceberg as far away as two miles and from the bottom at a depth of one mile before bad weather forced a halt to the tests.

It did not take naval experts long to realize that a device that could detect icebergs and hidden shoals could also detect enemy submarines. Soon after the Germans' first successes with submarine warfare, Fessenden was hard at work modifying his device to filter out unwanted echoes, making it more precise. Across the ocean, French and British scientists were also desperately at work to stave off the submarine menace. Thanks to the pressure of wartime necessity, sound-ranging equipment emerged from the war in greatly improved form.

By the mid-1920's practically all maritime nations either had their own echo sounders or had access to someone else's. Commercial ships were beginning to use them, and oceanographic expeditions employed them to make soundings at a rate that would have been impossible with the traditional lead and line. Some bugs still had to be worked out, however. Many soundings turned out to be inaccurate when checked by a weight and wire line. Disconcertingly, there was no pattern to the errors; they varied unpredictably. Tables on how the speed of sound underwater was affected by changes in the water's pressure, temperature, and salinity had to be painstakingly worked out before the echo sounder was truly accurate.

During the 1930's navy scientists and engineers improved the echo-sounding system, and when World War II broke out it was in wide use. The British called it ASDIC (Anti-Submarine Detection Investigation Committee); the United States called it Sound Navigation Ranging, or sonar for short.

Sonar-equipped ships turned up some interesting oceanographic phenomena during the war. They learned that schools of fish and whales could send back a sonar echo that falsely indicated a lurking submarine. Sonar readings sometimes registered shoals where the maps had none, and these shoals had a habit of disappearing as mysteriously as they appeared. Researchers found that these false sonar readings were caused by a mysterious "deep scattering layer" that sank during the daylight hours and rose toward the surface by dark. There was much speculation about the nature of the mysterious DSL, but not until the 1960's was its cause established: the soundings were being reflected by the swim bladders of huge schools of lantern fish, from the bells of jellyfish, and from certain species of shrimps.

Another discovery made by the men at the hydrophones was that the silent sea was really not silent at all. It was often filled with noises: boops, grunts, squeals, moans, clicks, and cracklings. This led to a good deal of fascinating underwater research after the war in the effort to identify these sounds. Some turned out to come from whales and dolphins; many were made by fish; some were even made by the snapping of shrimps' claws. Research is still going on to learn the function of these sounds and what messages, if any, they convey.

A Princeton geologist named Harry Hess, on wartime duty with the Navy, took regular echo soundings as his transport ship plowed back and forth across the Pacific. He discovered over one hundred curious flat-topped, sunken mountains whose existence had never been suspected because they lay from 1,800 to 6,000 feet below the surface. Hess named these puzzling sea forms *guyots,* in honor of Arnold Guyot, a Swiss-born geologist who had taught for thirty years at Princeton in the nineteenth century.

Postwar developments in sonar included a side-scanning sonar that permits submarines to "see" objects on either side and a forward-scanning sonar that reveals objects in the vessel's path. Such sonars, towed from a surface ship, have also been valuable in mapping the bottom. There is also a narrow-beam sonar, used for depth measurements, that gives much more precise measurements than the old broad-beam sonar.

Seismic profiling, another method of exploring the ocean floor, was developed during the 1930's. The pioneer was Maurice Ewing, a physics professor who had done seismic exploration work on land for oil companies. (Ewing's story will be covered in more detail in the section on the Lamont-Doherty Geological Observatory.) In dry-land seismic exploration, a charge of explosive is set off at a predetermined spot. The shock waves of the explosion race through the ground, bounce off the underlying layers of rock, and are picked up by an array of distant receivers connected to seismographs. The speed and strength of the reflected shock waves indicate what sort of rock underlies the ground in that area and give the geologists clues to whether or not oil is likely to be found there.

Seismic exploration at sea requires slightly different techniques. The shock waves are picked up by receivers on floats near the ship (but far enough away so that they are not affected by the vibrations of the ship's engines), but the basic principle is the same.

Since Ewing's work began, seismic exploration has come into worldwide use, by oil companies as well as by oceanographers. With a sophisticated technique known as multichannel seismics, it can now explore the ocean bedrock several layers deep. Computers interpret the results and give profiles in moments, although the computations would take months if done by hand.

Seismic methods are also used for depth soundings in water that is too deep for a sonar pinger to reach the bottom. Specially shaped charges that focus the shock waves permit more precise results. Many seismic experts have abandoned the hazardous use of explosives altogether and instead use an "air gun," a large device that uses compressed air at high pressure to create a powerful shock wave.

Biological oceanography entered a new phase in 1930, when William Beebe and Otis Barton made their first descent in the bathysphere, a pressure-resistant underwater observation chamber that the two men had designed. Beebe was an ornithologist who had become interested in undersea life; Barton was an engineer. On their first nonpractice dive, the men reached 800 feet; later dives took them as deep as 3,028 feet. On the first dive, Beebe was able to observe the gradual fading and disappearance of colors as the light waves of each length were successively absorbed by the water—the first man to do so. Beebe was also the first to observe live deep-sea organisms in their own environment, rather than mangled and dying in a net.

In 1942 two Frenchmen, Jacques-Yves Cousteau and Emile Gagnan, invented the aqualung, the forerunner of all today's scuba devices. *Scuba* stands for Self-Contained Underwater Breathing Apparatus, and its invention was a breakthrough in more ways than one. Scuba made it possible for sportsmen to go exploring and spearfishing underwater, but it also made it possible for scientists for the first time to observe underwater life close up under natural conditions. (The bathysphere, great step forward though it was, kept observers imprisoned in one spot and dependent on the marine animals approaching them. With scuba gear, an observer can go where he wants and follow the fish.)

Cousteau and his associates also pioneered in the development of research submersibles, small unarmed submarines especially designed for scientific operations. Equipped with floodlights and cameras, submersibles not only bring scientists down to depths that a diver cannot reach, but bring back a photographic record of marine life, geological formations, and current marks on the bottom. If equipped with a mechanical claw they can perform such tasks as planting current meters, bringing back samples of rock, or retrieving fragments of a wrecked submarine. And, of course, they can compile a complete record of the temperature, pressure, and salinity of the water at every level throughout the dive—the data so dear to the hearts of physical oceanographers.

Despite the disadvantage of very limited range, submersibles are extremely useful for oceanographic research. Unfortunately, they also cost about $10,000 a day to operate. The result has been that, after a few years of activity in the late 1960's, submersibles are at present used only for infrequent, very special assignments.

Another technological breakthrough that Cousteau helped to develop is the underwater habitat, a chamber that scientists, technicians, and sport divers can use as a base and living quarters for periods up to a month while they perform their underwater tasks. The advantage of the habitat is that the divers do not need to return to the surface when their breathing supply runs low, and so do not need to go through the lengthy, time-consuming process of decompression at the end of each dive.

Decompression is needed for deep dives because the diver must get his breathing supply at a pressure equal to that of the water around him. Otherwise the pressure of the water on his chest would prevent him from breathing. Under high pressure, the diver's body tissues absorb gases from the breathing mixture. If the pressure on the diver's body is reduced too suddenly, the gases come bubbling out of the solution like the fizz in a bottle of soda pop. The result is excruciating pain, paralysis, or even death. But if the pressure is reduced gradually, the dissolved gases pass out of the diver's tissues slowly and gently, and no harm is done. The only drawback is that decompression takes so long. For example, a diver who has spent one hour at a depth of 300 feet must spend 7.63 hours in decompression—over seven and one half times his working time. Thus the invention of the habitat added precious hours of productive diving time.

The idea of the habitat was born in the 1950's when a U.S. Navy doctor, Captain George Bond, developed the concept of saturation diving. For some time it had been known that, once a diver had spent a certain time at a given depth, the gases dissolved in his blood reached a saturation point. That is, no matter how much longer he stayed down at that depth, his blood would not absorb any more gas. Unfortunately, the deeper a diver goes, the more rapidly he becomes chilled by the water and exhausted by the stress of working under high pressure. Bond reasoned that, if a diver had a pressurized chamber down on the bottom where he could go to rest and warm up between dives, his working time could be extended indefinitely.

Bond proposed such a chamber to his Navy superiors, but was turned down. The idea was picked up by Cousteau, an old acquaintance of Bond, who was interested in his work. Cousteau's first habitat, dubbed *Conshelf-I,* was installed on the seafloor near Marseilles, France, in 1962, at a depth of 33 feet. A select crew of divers spent a week there at twice normal atmospheric pressure with no ill effects.

Cousteau's success inspired an American inventor, Edwin Link, to send a man to a depth of 200 feet in a chamber of Link's design. Again, the experiment was largely successful, although the diver almost had an attack of the bends as he went through his end-of-dive decompression on his mother ship. A series of habitats followed—two more *Conshelfs*, the U.S. Navy's SEALABs I and II (a third SEALAB had to be scrapped because of technical failures that resulted in a diver's death), the shallow-water TEKTITE, sponsored in part by NASA to test men's capabilities of working for long periods in isolation. TEKTITE thus served as a pilot project for the first space missions. This was not the only connection between oceanography and space travel, for one of the principal directors of SEALAB II was a former astronaut, M. Scott Carpenter. TEKTITE was also the base for another precedent-breaking project: a two-week underwater sojourn by an all-female scientific team. There were also small, easily portable habitats such as the Perry *Hydrolab* and the University of New Hampshire's EDALHAB. Japan, the Soviet Union, Britain, and West Germany have also developed their own habitats.

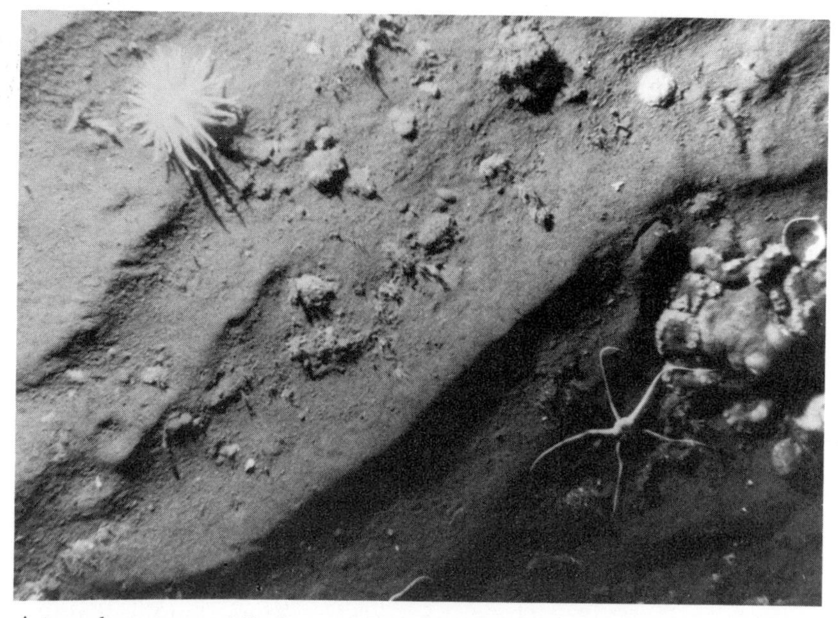

A towed camera and flash reveal ripple marks and deep-sea bottom-dwelling animals in the South Atlantic. Brittle stars and sea anemones appear to dominate the benthic (bottom-dwelling) fauna in this photograph.

Lamont-Doherty Geological Observatory

But it is not always possible to send scientists down in a habitat or a submersible to make observations. Instead, many institutions use submerged TV cameras towed from a ship. These give a fairly clear view of the bottom and also record it on videotape. So far, they work only in black-and-white, for color is too expensive. But even a black-and-white visual record of the bottom is a lot more informative than none at all.

Oceanographers also make use of space technology. Orbiting satellites perform such invaluable tasks as transmitting TV pictures of weather patterns, photographing currents, and mapping coastlines. In addition, satellite-mounted equipment can establish sea levels with a degree of accuracy never before obtainable, locate icebergs, and even show the true shape of the planet Earth.

Another recently developed technique for gathering information about the oceans is deep-sea drilling. Deep-sea drilling uses the same kind of equipment as an oil derrick, but instead of having a drill tower firmly planted on the solid earth, its drilling platform is a rolling, pitching ship. The goals are different, too. The oil driller wants to get petroleum, and the layers of dirt and rock that he must grind his way through to reach it are just an annoyance. The scientist drilling the floor of the deep sea is interested in the cores he brings up through his hollow drill bit and pipe. These cores, composed of rocks and sediments, reveal the biography of the sea and give evidence of climatic conditions of bygone eras.

The most-used type of corer, however, is the piston corer, a much simpler and more easily handled device than the drill. Its basic parts are a hollow pipe about three inches in diameter, a massive lead weight, a movable piston inside the pipe, and a flap valve at the bottom end of the pipe. In use, the corer is lowered over the side of a ship, and its weight (well over half a ton) carries it down into the soft sediments of the seafloor. As the corer sinks into the seafloor, the piston inside it moves up and sucks in a long column of sediment. When the corer is pulled up, the flap valve at its lower end closes and keeps the sediment from falling out. (The friction of the tightly packed muck against the pipe is usually enough to keep the core in place, but the valve makes it almost impossible to lose a core. In this way, it is possible to secure core samples up to 30 meters in length (nearly 100 feet). Such long cores are obtained by screwing sections of corer pipe together.

The coring tube is an old device, going back to the days of the *Challenger*. But the amount of sediment that a simple tube can bring back is limited. The piston corer, invented by the Swedish scientist Börje Kullenberg in the 1940's, made it possible to get longer cores. But Kullenberg's corer was a delicate, easily damaged instrument. An improved version was invented in 1948 by

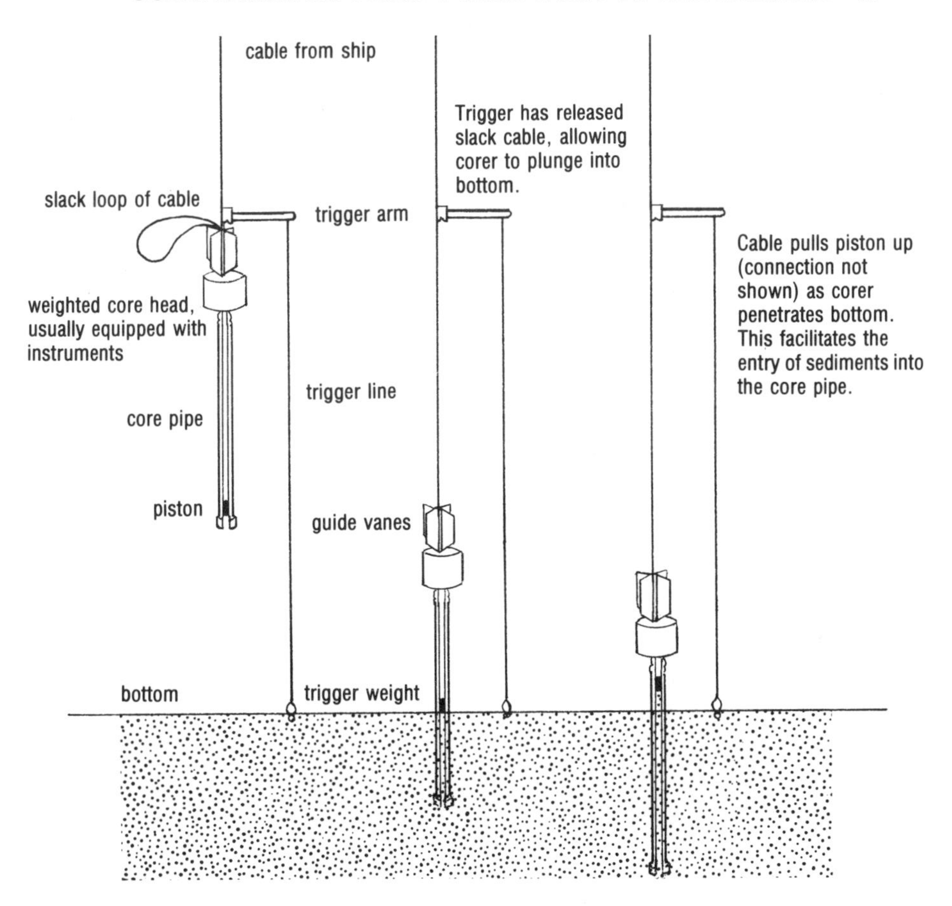

Diagram showing the operation of a Ewing piston corer

Adapted from a drawing furnished by Lamont-Doherty Geological Observatory

Maurice Ewing, an insatiable tinkerer. Ewing's corer was made of ordinary boiler tubing, so that sections were readily interchangeable, and it was no great loss if one was damaged by hitting rock instead of mud. He also increased the corer's penetrating power by hanging it from an attachment that left a long loop of line slack just above the corer. A simple trigger device contacted the sea floor while the corer was still a good distance above it, released the slack, and let the corer plunge down.

Probably the most momentous development of this century in geology is the theory of seafloor spreading and plate tectonics, which revolutionized our thinking about the geological history of the Earth and the formation of the continents. The decisive proof of this theory was supplied by deep-sea drilling core samples from the ocean floor.

The story goes back to 1912, when Alfred Wegener proposed his theory of continental drift. The German's proposal was greeted with universal scorn, as it seemed to contradict all the evidence that geologists had gathered up to then. Critics sneered that Wegener was not even a geologist, but a meteorologist. As late as the 1950's, if a university geologist wanted to keep his job, he dared not support the idea of continental drift. But by the end of the fifties the situation changed. A growing number of scientists leaned more and more toward the theory that the world's continents had once all been part of a super-giant landmass that broke up ages ago, and that since then they have been drifting into new and changing configurations across the planet's surface.

Geologists began to turn up an increasing amount of evidence that seemed to support the theory that the continents had once been joined. Still, no one came up with a completely convincing explanation of how this happened. The most workable theory went like this: The continents are composed of relatively light rocks that "float" on the heavier rocks of the underlying crust of the Earth. The crust is divided into jagged-edged sections, or plates, that move about on the semiliquid layer of rock beneath them, the mantle. As the plates move, they carry the continents around on their backs.

This raised some questions of what happened where two plates nosed up against each other, and what happened where they pulled apart. According to the theory, when two plates meet, one slides beneath the other and makes a long, slow dive deep into the mantle. Along the edges where they pull apart, as they seemed to be doing along the Mid-Ocean Ridge, new rock material wells up from below to become part of a spreading seafloor. Seismic profiles taken by geological oceanographers appeared to support this hypothesis. Magnetometers towed by oceanographic research vessels eventually provided the clincher. At intervals, the Earth's magnetic field reverses itself, and these reversals are recorded in the magnetism of the rocks that are formed at the time. Over a wide band on either side of the Mid-Ocean Rift, the magnetic orientation of rocks and sediments matched perfectly. Normal polarity alternated with reversed polarity in a pattern almost as regular as wallpaper. This pattern could have been created in only one way—by a spreading seafloor. The proof was complete.

But the study of plate tectonics is far from over. Many basic questions remain unanswered. And it is almost certain that the answers will come from the work of oceanographers.

4

How Marine Science Institutions Evolved

Late as the marine sciences were in developing, institutions that specialized in them were even later on the scientific scene. A small biological station was established at Marseilles, France, as early as 1834, but very few others were built until the 1870's. Until then, practically all marine research was done by navy vessels, government bureaus, and scholars at universities. Museums also played a part. There naturalists could go to examine preserved specimens (dried, pickled, or atrociously stuffed) and compare them against their own catches.

One reason for the lack of marine-science institutions was doubtless the undeveloped state of marine science until after the mid-1800's. Another was lack of public interest and therefore of money. The 1800's were the great age of industrial expansion. Governments, and sometimes rich men with a sense of public responsibility, founded engineering schools and endowed chairs of chemistry and physics at the universities, for these were plainly helpful to business. But investigating the sea—except for mapping reefs, shoals, winds, and currents, which was helpful to transportation—was another matter entirely. Thus, when the Belgian scientist Pierre-Joseph van Beneden founded his country's first marine-science laboratory in 1842, he had to do it out of his own pocket. Perhaps this is just an example of official Belgian parsimony, for the Belgian Antarctic Expedition of 1897–99 almost never got away from the pier at Antwerp for lack of money. Only a frantic, last-minute appeal to Antwerp's wealthiest citizens saved the expedition.

But that is jumping ahead in time. Marine-science institutions got their real start in 1872, when a German zoologist named Anton Dohrn founded the Stazione Zoologica (Zoological Station) in Naples, Italy. Dohrn was not only a good zoologist but also an inventive and dynamic administrator, qualities that are absolutely indispensable for the success of any marine-science institution. It was Dohrn who came up with the idea of installing "tables" (actually work areas) in his laboratories that governments, universities, or other organizations could rent for their people to use. The income from these rental fees not only maintained the lab but also paid for collecting boats that went out daily to gather specimens for the researchers. Dohrn also created a public aquarium that was a great drawing card. The Stazione Zoologica became the successful prototype for a whole network of marine field stations, where scientists and students could come to do special projects for which their own institutions lacked the facilities. These field stations served the marine-science community until the early 1970's, when many of them were forced to close down for lack of funds.

Even earlier than Dohrn's Zoological Station was the oceanographic school of the University of Kiel, in northwestern Germany, founded in 1870. However, it was not so immediately influential. Although it did creditable work in investigating the marine life of the Baltic and North Seas, it was not an international gathering place for scientists.

However, Dohrn's example was followed in country after country. A marine biological station was founded at Kristineberg, on Sweden's west coast, in 1877. In 1879 the Marine Biological Association of the United Kingdom was founded at Plymouth, England. In 1888 the Marine Biological Laboratory (MBL) was founded at Woods Hole, Massachusetts, where the U.S. Fish Commission had already been operating for several years.

The MBL was designed to be a summer institute on the lines of a short-lived school that the famous Harvard professor of natural history, Louis Agassiz, had set up on Penikese Island, near Woods Hole, in 1873. Forty students, most of them young teachers, enrolled the first summer. In theory, the Penikese school was a brilliant new idea. Experts came to lecture on a variety of subjects, from deep-sea animals to embryology, fossils, and how to use a microscope. There were almost as many courses as there were students (interestingly, sixteen of the forty students were women, no mean figure for an era when women were not encouraged to acquire higher knowledge).

But the problems were too great. The school had opened without proper preparation, foul-ups occurred, and Professor Agassiz himself died that December. Penikese Island was uninhabited, so that all supplies had to come from the mainland, and it was also hard to reach. None of Agassiz' associates wanted to take on the responsibility of operating a school under such conditions, and after struggling through one more summer the school was discontinued.

Unlike Penikese, the Marine Biological Laboratory was a solid success, with courses, research projects, and field trips. And, being privately run, it did not depend on the yearly generosity of the federal government or the state legislature. As a result, it was safe for investigators to start long-term projects there, knowing that the institution would still be in operation the next year.

While "pure" science founded some of the early marine-science labs, the need for fishery research was responsible for more. The tasks of fishery-research institutes varied widely, though they all conducted fish censuses and piled up statistics of the catches by fishermen of their nations. In its early years, for example, the U.S. Fish Commission's main job was running fish hatcheries. In Denmark, the director of the country's first biological station sampled plankton, donned diving gear to inspect oyster beds, and experimented with harvesting mussels for chicken feed.

This enterprising Dane, C. G. Johannes Petersen, also invented the fish tag, an invaluable tool for all studies of fish populations. Fish look so much alike that it is impossible to tell one flounder or herring from another, to distinguish one individual cod from the other cod in the school, and so on. Petersen hit on the idea of tagging fish with a pair of bone buttons, connected by a thin strand of silver wire that ran through the fish's back. (The same technique is used today, except that plastic buttons have taken the place of bone.) The buttons were marked with the date and place of tagging. With this identification, biologists were able to study the growth rates of the fish, trace their migrations, and make a pretty close estimate of their survival rates.

Here again is an example of how a simple invention made possible a giant step forward in oceanographic research. Petersen's achievements seem all the more remarkable when we consider the fact that for years his entire institution was contained on a wooden ship's hull that was towed from place to place.

The Kiel oceanographic school was also involved in fishery

research and became noted for its investigations of plankton. In fact, it was the school's founder, Victor Hensen, who coined the word *plankton* in 1887.

Like the MBL at Woods Hole, the other early marine-research institutions in the United States were devoted to marine biology and gradually expanded their spheres of interest. The famous Scripps Institution of Oceanography began as an unofficial branch of the zoology department of the University of California in 1905, with the specific goal of investigating the marine life off the coast of Southern California. It was to have particular concentration on plankton. Not until 1908 did the institution acquire a physical oceanographer, and then only to provide information on the environments where the plankton were found. It was soon realized that physical oceanography was a worthwhile field of study in its own right, but physical oceanography remained subordinate until the 1920's. About that time, Scripps made its first tentative moves into chemical oceanography. Not until 1924, under a new director recruited from the U.S. Geological Survey, did Scripps begin to do work in geological oceanography, a field in which it is now renowned.

Many of the newer marine-science institutions have a similar story. The Graduate School of Oceanography of the University of Rhode Island began as the marine biological lab of an obscure New England agricultural college; it is now one of the leading marine institutions in the United States, involved in all fields of oceanography and even leading in the oceanography-related field of marine affairs (of which more later). The Virginia Institute of Marine Science originated as a part of the state fisheries commission; it is now outstanding in coastal and estuarine work of all sorts. These few examples illustrate the general pattern; there are many more.

The 1930's saw the founding of the Woods Hole Oceanographic Institution, the Duke University Marine Laboratory, the University of Rhode Island's Narragansett Marine Laboratory, and a handful of other marine institutions. But the real expansion of marine-science institutions in the United States, as elsewhere, had to wait until after World War II.

During the war, the existing oceanographic institutions took on a new importance, for only they had the special knowledge of the seas that the warring nations needed for naval operations, particularly for submarine warfare. In the United States, for example, the gentle marine biologist Mary Sears, of Woods Hole, found herself teaching submarine commanders how to hide under the thermocline. The thermocline is the boundary layer between two water masses of different temperatures. It is usually quite sharply defined, as seawater of different temperatures or salinities tends not to mix. For submariners, a thermocline has a property of special importance—it refracts sonar waves like a prism. A sub pursued by enemy vessels had only to find the thermocline, slip under, and cut its motors. There it could lie in silence, undetectable by sonar or hydrophones. Submariners also learned about the kinds of bottom that could give confusing sonar echoes, about subsurface currents that could carry their vessels unexpectedly up or down, about variations in temperature or density that could play hell with a sub's delicately regulated buoyancy, and about other arcane but important matters.

A tool with which submarine commanders (and subchasers too) could detect thermoclines was the bathythermograph. This is an instrument that measures water temperature and depth simultaneously (the depth is calculated from the water pressure). Invented in the late 1930's by the prolific scientist Athelstan Spilhaus, the bathythermograph was soon improved by Maurice Ewing, Allyn Vine, and John Worzel. The BT, as it is usually called, is one of the workhorses of modern oceanography.

With a pistol-like device, a scientist launches an XBT (expendable bathythermograph) from Lamont-Doherty's R/V *Conrad* into the Antarctic Ocean. The instrument provides data on temperatures in the upper 1,000 meters (3,300 feet) of the ocean.

Lamont-Doherty Geological Observatory

Oceanographers were also pressed into service to solve the puzzling "afternoon effect" that threw echo-sounding gear wildly off the mark. Sonar trials during the 1930's had revealed that although the sonar could easily detect a submarine during the morning, by afternoon it failed to pick up the target even when it was directly over the sub. The answer turned out to be that the sun's heat warmed the surface waters much more than the deeper layers, thereby creating a thermocline that refracted sonar waves and bent them far off course.

This discovery led oceanographers into experiments to devise more effective sonars that would detect thermoclines and predict when they would occur, and to work up refraction tables that would enable sonar operators to compensate for thermocline effects. It also led them into the brand-new field of submarine acoustics, which became a major area of investigation.

Another subject that became vital was wave forecasting, which was needed for landing troops and equipment at beachheads. Too rough a sea meant trouble in putting men and matériel ashore, or even disaster. Wave forecasting allowed commanders to pick the most favorable times for landings.

In the Pacific, many islands were insufficiently mapped. American invasion forces came to grief on reefs that the maps—some of them a century old—did not show. An oceanographic crew was given the task of putting together the scattered fragments of information that had been received before the war and making sense of them. They correlated waves and swells, currents, diving conditions, bottom sediments, bottom topography, temperature, salinity, visibility conditions of the water, and similar data for scores of obscure Pacific islands and atolls.

Oceanographers made an invaluable contribution to the war effort, and the war effort created many new jobs for oceanographers. But just as the Navy's oceanographic program really got rolling, the war ended. Hundreds of oceanographers found themselves back on the civilian job market, while their institutions found themselves threatened by the end of government funding. It was obvious that they could not go back to the prewar system of private support. To do so would have condemned them to "creekology"—studying only the easily accessible offshore waters near their institutions. As one knowledgeable oceanographer puts it, without government money you would end up with a mob of scientists fighting each other for elbow room on the pier.

The result was that, in order to continue operating, the oceanographic institutions had to solicit government research contracts, which is still the system under which they operate today. This profoundly affected the nature of oceanographic research, since it meant that government officials, rather than the scientists themselves, had the final say on what would be done. It also definitely ended the dominance of biology over the other branches of oceanography and gave a boost to physical oceanography and its subdivision of air-sea interactions. Geological oceanography benefited immensely from government contracts, too.

The new instruments developed during the war and the information amassed by scientists doing wartime assignments led to an explosive growth of oceanographic investigations during the postwar years. Much of the research was military. Much was done by oil companies searching for new petroleum reserves on the continental shelves. The research that the public found most interesting was in biology, due largely to the superb dramatic flair of Jacques-Yves Cousteau. More than any other factor, it was Cousteau's poetic books and beautifully made films that put oceanography on the map. Cousteau has been severely criticized by the scientific community for everything from taking credit for other people's ideas to presenting a false and highly romanticized picture of oceanographic research. This writer is not in a position to judge the validity of these accusations. But even if they were 100 percent true, Cousteau would still deserve great credit—for making the public aware of oceanography, for his work as an educator and as a dedicated conservationist, and for furthering the development and promotion of scuba gear, submersibles, and habitats.

Whether because of Cousteau's influence or not, oceanographic institutions began to acquire more and larger research vessels. Prewar research vessels had been converted yachts, beautiful to see and to sail, but woefully short of room for scientists, collecting gear, and storage space for specimens. After the war, the institutions began to acquire secondhand navy boats such as minesweepers. These vessels, though not designed for comfort or stability, were at least roomier than yachts and had a longer cruising range. But they were far from ideal for scientific purposes. Beginning in the late 1960's, institutions began to replace them with vessels designed especially for oceanographic research. The new generation of research vessels typically has the bridge far forward to leave a large, clear deck space, a sturdy A-frame overhanging the stern for pulling in trawls and dredges, swiveling booms over the sides for coring gear, bathythermographs, and small nets, and winches large and small. The more advanced vessels have a bow thruster—a swiveling propeller mounted under the bow that pushes it to one side or another and thus makes possible very precise control of the ship's position.

The laboratory quarters are designed so that entire workbenches with all their scientific gear can be installed, dismounted at the end of a voyage, and replaced with another scientist's bench and specialized equipment for another type of work. Some institutions increase their lab space by using portable modules called vans, modeled on the lines of freight containers. The vans, complete with equipment, are swung up on deck by a crane, bolted down in their assigned positions, and quickly hooked up to water and electric power lines. At the end of the voyage, they are easily dismounted and the decks left clear.

Equipment at an oceanographic institution usually includes an array of computers, in many cases linked to a computer center where the more complex programs can be run through. Like most fields of modern science, oceanography depends increasingly on computer models. Typical problems are water exchange in an estuary, wave dynamics, and the effect on fish populations of dumping large amounts of dredging spoil on the seafloor. Then there are electron microscopes that can enlarge an object more than a million times and scanning electron microscopes that are capable of a 500,000-power magnification, with a three-dimensional effect. There are mass spectrometers, gas chromatographs, and a large array of other sophisticated analytical devices.

Much of the work of chemical oceanographers consists of analyzing water samples for traces of pollutants, such as heavy metals or PCBs, kepone, and other chlorinated hydrocarbons. Since scientists must often do these analyses on a level of *parts per million,* the slightest contamination from the outside can throw the whole test off. So the scientist does his testing in an ultraclean laboratory. For metal analyses, he uses a lab in which all the plumbing and fittings are of plastic. Even the walls are coated with plastic to prevent tiny amounts of metallic pigments from paint from getting into the sample and contaminating it. For detecting organic chemicals, such as the chlorinated hydrocarbons, he uses a lab with fittings of stainless steel. As an extra precaution, all work on the samples is done in a special enclosure where a current of highly filtered air wafts dust and other impurities away and out.

Dust is one of the chief enemies in the ultraclean lab, for it brings in traces of contaminants that can render a whole analysis faulty. Lead is a good example. It is present in many bodies of water near urban areas on a scale of parts per million. Thanks to the exhaust of millions of gasoline engines, it is present in ordinary street dust on a scale ten thousand times greater. Analytical chemists work with small samples, so that if a speck of lead-bearing dust settles into a test tube of seawater, it gives much too high a reading for lead concentration.

To avoid such contamination, the lab is pressurized with filtered air; whenever anyone opens the door to enter or leave, the clean air inside the lab chamber pushes the dust-laden outside air away. It is impractical to wear special dust-free coveralls in the lab. They are uncomfortable and constricting, and a person wearing one soon tends to lose his accuracy. But street clothes are covered by a dustproof smock, and instead of their street shoes, the lab workers must wear special footgear of a nonparticulating material—one that does not give off tiny flakes. Heads must also be covered, and in theory beards should be enclosed in some kind of dustproof wrap. However, the many bearded scientists rarely bother to go to this length. As one pointed out to me, the really ultraclean part of the lab is under the hoods where the actual work is done, and beards do not get in under there.

But it is not equipment that makes a great research institution. It is the scientists. A topflight marine scientist must be intelligent, of course. He must be imaginative enough to think of new fields of investigation and persistent enough to follow a project for years, until he has piled up enough data to base a valid conclusion on. And the scientist must be willing to accept a fair percentage of failures in his search for truth. (Perhaps I should say he or she, for a growing number of marine scientists are women.)

During the flush times of the 1960's, the marine sciences bloomed like plankton in springtime. A number of universities in the United States added oceanographic or marine-science divisions. Others added courses in oceanographic subjects. From a mere dozen or so in the early 1960's, the number of institutions that offer twenty-five or more semester hours in marine-related disciplines has risen to about 170. Some are in such landlocked locations as Missouri and Arizona. Even discounting those schools that specialize in areas such as ship design, there are probably a good 150 involved in one way or another with ocean research.

A significant development for oceanographic institutions was the establishment of the National Sea Grant program in 1966. Very briefly, Sea Grant's role is to funnel federal money to colleges and universities to pay for research programs. Like the other major sources of funding, the Office of Naval Research and the National Science Foundation, Sea Grant pays the salaries of scientists and their assistants (usually graduate students who earn and learn at the same time), foots the bill for equipment, and even pays for research voyages. (We will discuss the Sea Grant program in greater detail in a later chapter.) The University of Rhode

Island, the University of Delaware, Oregon State University, the University of Wisconsin, and Texas A & M are among the schools with large and active Sea Grant programs.

One of the things that distinguish Sea Grant projects from others is that they must offer some tangible benefit to the nation or to the world. In other words, they must pay off in economic or social terms. Sea Grant does not subsidize the pursuit of knowledge for its own sake. This "practical" approach greatly bothers some old-line oceanographers, who like to point out that so-called "pure" science more often than not produces some highly useful and profitable spin-offs. On the other hand, it is also true that when a scientist is handed the task of some "applied" research, he usually has to do some pretty fundamental research in the process.

Regardless of the merits and demerits of "pure" versus "applied" research, oceanography and the marine sciences in general have been increasingly influenced by the idea that research must have some social justification. Another development of some consequence is that most marine-science institutions serve as consultants to the community. They do this on all levels from international bodies down to the county or town level, and they serve individuals as well. The Stony Brook, Long Island, branch of SUNY (the State University of New York) is a good example. Faculty member Dr. J. L. McHugh served with distinction for years on the International Whaling Commission. At the same time, other faculty members advised the Town of Hempstead and other nearby town governments on the probable consequences of dredging, building marinas, and other man-made changes in the marine environment. They also furnished advice to local clammers and fishermen.

Technology has seen some exciting advances, and many discoveries yet remain to be made. Oceanographic institutions will play a leading role in these discoveries.

5

A Day at an Oceanographic Institution

I had originally planned to make this chapter a report of an actual day at an actual institution, giving a panoramic view of the activities, until I found out that there is just too much going on to cover in a single chapter. Instead, I will try to give a condensed, composite picture based on what I have observed and what students, scientists, administrators, and others have told me.

On a typical day, any or all of the following activities may be occurring. Scientists are planning research cruises, working on data and samples from the last cruise, and writing papers on the results. They are also likely to be writing up proposals for new projects to submit for funding. Depending on the particular scientist's commitments, he or she may also be setting up an experiment or checking up on its progress, conferring with student advisees, and giving a lecture. Sometimes it is necessary to update the lectures to keep abreast of current developments. The hard-pressed scientist must also scan the current literature in his field to stay in touch with what other researchers are doing. Although scientists accept the responsibility of teaching students, and most of them enjoy it, they are always glad to have a term without teaching chores so that they can get on with their own research.

About one hour in every five of a marine scientist's time is taken up with some sort of paperwork. At the peak paperwork season, shortly before the deadline for submitting proposals, it may take as much as 80 percent of the scientist's time. No one is happy with this situation, but until the day when all scientists can afford to pay for their own research, there really doesn't seem to be any alternative. Governments and foundations cannot afford to hand out money unless they have a good idea of where that money is going, and whether or not it will yield a worthwhile result. They cannot know this without a detailed, written proposal from the scientist who is applying for a grant.

Technicians and lab assistants are processing data and samples, cataloging new samples as they come in, and helping with experiments. They may also be preparing and running computer programs.

Students are doing reading for their course work and for their own investigations, attending classes, and conducting experiments. Some of their most fruitful time is spent exchanging ideas with fellow students.

Down at the shops, engineers and skilled workmen are busy designing and building new equipment for work at sea, such as instrument buoys, STD (salinity, temperature, and depth) meters, and plankton collectors. A major part of the working day at the shops goes into repairing and maintaining existing equipment. A well-equipped institutional shop has woodworking and metal-working machine tools and hand tools, welding torches, a plastic shop, and facilities for fine work such as electronics. Much of the shop is used for storing oceanographic equipment.

At the pier, a research vessel may be loading for a cruise or unloading after completing a voyage. Loading is a hectic procedure, what with having to make sure that all the equipment and supplies get on board in time and stowed in the correct place. Unloading is a bit more leisurely, although no time is wasted. After everything loose is unloaded, the shipboard laboratories must be dismantled and carried ashore to make room for the equipment needed by the next group of scientists scheduled to go out.

An important component of the marine-science or oceanographic institution's activity, though given little notice by writers, is administration and maintenance. There must be secretaries and clerks to handle the vast flow of correspondence, reports, and other typing and filing. Deans and department heads are needed to ride herd on day-to-day and year-to-year operations and keep things in running order. Although I have heard scientists deplore the growing ratio of administrators to working scientists in many

Launching an STD probe (salinity, temperature, and depth) from R/V *Eltanin*. Surrounding the probe are a battery of bottles, operated by an electrical signal from the surface, for collecting water samples at different depths.
Lamont-Doherty Geological Observatory

institutions, I have also heard the complaint that there weren't administrators enough and that the situation was deteriorating into chaos. Someone must balance the competing claims of researchers for money and space.

Without the maintenance staff, the institution would literally fall apart. Though their work deals with such humdrum matters as fixing a leaky roof or replacing a defective water pipe, or installing lab benches, sinks, and lighting, it is vital. A carefully planned experiment can be ruined by the failure of the water supply at a crucial point, or by the electrical system's conking out.

The day often begins early, before the official opening hour. Scientists and students who are setting up an experiment or checking on its progress, or who have paperwork to get out of the way, may come in at 7:30 or even earlier. If they don't have such pressing commitments or classes to meet, they straggle in as late as ten o'clock—oceanographic institutions pride themselves on their lack of regimentation. Self-interest ensures that the work gets done.

It often seems that an ocean scientist's day is nothing but interruptions. There are departmental conferences scheduled and unscheduled, and urgent calls from the administration when unforeseen problems pop up. There are phone calls from colleagues who want to borrow a piece of equipment, or from the departmental secretary who wants to know if Scientist X knows where Mr. Y or Ms. Z can be located. If the scientist has made a reputation in his field, he may be called away to help solve an emergency at another institution. For example, a marine seismologist may have to drop his work to help his colleagues at another institution repair their failing seismographic system. An outsider may wonder how the work of the institution ever gets done, but somehow it does.

I will add a brief sketch of the days of an actual student and scientist to make the picture clearer. The student is Alina Froelich, a marine biologist who was pursuing her doctorate at the Graduate School of Oceanography of the University of Rhode Island. I met Alina outside her laboratory building on a warm, sunny August afternoon. Dressed in shorts and a sport shirt, she was hosing out some mud-fouled lengths of plastic water pipe with her lab partner, a slender, gray-haired Belgian biologist named Thierry Jacques.

Alina did her undergraduate work in marine biology at the University of Puerto Rico and went on to advanced studies at Scripps. While there, she was chosen as one of the team of women aquanauts who spent fourteen days in an underwater habitat off the Virgin Islands, as part of Project TEKTITE II. The team conducted a wide range of biological studies; Alina's project was an investigation of the escape reactions of fish. Eventually, she came to URI to do her doctoral work.

Shortly after I introduced myself to her, a maintenance man approached and began upbraiding her and her partner for messing up the pipes with their dirt. Alina tried to explain that it was nothing they had done on purpose or through carelessness, but that mud and mussels had gotten into the intake system somehow during a recent storm. Somewhat mollified, the man subsided into a resentful mutter, helped them clean the outflow pipe, and stalked off.

When calm had been restored, we entered the small, cluttered laboratory room, most of which was occupied by a large tank of seawater and smaller, traylike tanks with experimental organisms in them. Alina explained her project to me. She and her partner were working on a joint investigation of a kind of hard coral called *Astrangia,* which happens to be the only kind of coral that grows in New England's coastal waters. (It does not form reefs, only little, stony chunks.) *Astrangia* is also interesting to biologists because some of its polyps (the individual animals that make up a coral colony) have brown algae living in them in a symbiotic relationship, while other polyps in the same colony may not. Plenty of corals have symbiotic algae, but this patchy distribution of algae is a biological oddity.

Alina showed me her specimens, unprepossessing to my layman's eye. Some were brown all over; some were white because they lacked the symbiotic algae; some were patchy brown and white. Her research mission was to study the metabolic interactions between the algae and the corals—in other words, to find out what each partner contributed to the growth and well-being of the other. For example, the carbon dioxide given off by the coral polyps is taken up by the algae and used by them in photosynthesis. The algae in turn give off sugars that help to feed the coral animals. They may also give off vitamins and enzymes that help the coral grow. She was particularly interested in comparing the metabolic interactions of her northern corals with those of a tropical reef. Her co-worker was studying the effects of changes in light and temperature on the growth rates of the same corals.

With her course work completed, Alina began her day at 9:30 by checking on her corals and making sure that conditions in the tank were satisfactory. Three days a week she fed them their rations of frozen brine shrimp. Corals are carnivorous—the only flesh-eating rock in the world. After seeing to the welfare of her experimental subjects, she might work with the electron microscope, studying the ultrastructure of thin slices of her corals. (Ultrastructure is cellular biologists' cant for the smallest structures in the cells, so called because you need ultrahigh magnification to see them.) She also prepared her own coral samples, cutting thin sections, mounting them on small copper grids, and staining them. Under the microscope, she could then see how the cells with algae living in them differed from those without algae. Alternatively, she might go to the nearby EPA (Environmental

Protection Agency) laboratory to work on coral histology (the study of the structure and chemical makeup of living tissues). Except in summer, she worked until 5:30 or 6:30 in the evening, often coming back to the lab or the library after supper to put in a few more hours of work or reading. Frequently her experiments required twelve to eighteen hours a day for several days in a row. Nevertheless, she managed to spend some time each day with her husband, a chemical oceanography student.

I learned about a scientist's typical day from Harold O'Connors, a genial, portly redhead from Oregon who is teaching and researching in biological oceanography at the Marine Sciences Research Center of the State University of New York at Stony Brook, Long Island. I called on Dr. O'Connors on a bitterly cold January day, during a period when school was out and there were very few students around. Since he had no classes to prepare for, he felt that he could give me a true picture of the scientific work of his school, as distinct from the educational side.

Dr. O'Connors had come in at 7:30, his usual time, to set up an experiment for a project he was conducting for the New York State ERDA (Energy Resources Development Agency). The goal of the project, on which he was collaborating with two other scientists from Stony Brook, was to ascertain the environmental impact of a new kind of construction block made of ash and stabilized scrubber wastes from coal-burning electric-power plants. (The scrubber is a filter device in a smokestack that traps fine particles of ash and other substances in the hot waste gases that pass through the stack. Scrubbers can also be designed to take out certain components of the gases themselves, such as sulfur dioxide.) Since one use planned for these blocks was for building seaside retaining walls, piers, and similar structures, and since they were known to contain small amounts of heavy metals and other toxic substances, it was necessary to find out whether they would harm marine life and how they would hold up under exposure to seawater before they could be cleared for use.

Dr. O'Connors' teammates were a chemical oceanographer, Dr. Ivar Duedall, and a marine geochemist, Dr. Ramesh Dayal. The latter two were to do a chemical analysis of the ash blocks and ascertain how they interacted chemically with seawater and sediments. While these scientists established what leached out of the blocks and how much of it was absorbed into the sediments of the bottom, O'Connors' role was to test the toxicity of the blocks.

His plan was simple—to take a culture of a plankton organism, the diatom *Thalassiosira pseudonana,* and expose it to a solution of the waste with nutrients added. The mixture was spiked with a radioactive tracer, carbon-14, so that he could easily measure the rate of photosynthesis by the amount of radioactive carbon these diatoms absorbed during photosynthesis. Test tubes of diatoms in a nutrient solution containing C-14, but without the waste solution prepared from the ash blocks, served as controls. By comparing differences in the rates of photosynthesis in the two batches, he could see whether any of the soluble components contained in the ash blocks had a significant effect on plankton growth.

On the day of my visit, Dr. O'Connors and his assistant were doing a test run of the experiment, to perfect their procedures and techniques. I watched while they added carbon-14 tracer solution to the diatom broth in the radioactive lab, then carried off the containers to O'Connors' own lab around the corner. The test tubes were allowed to incubate for two hours before the assay to measure C-14 uptake. Additional samples of the diatom culture were passed through an electronic particle counter to get an estimate of the number of diatom cells present in a given volume. From this, it was simple to calculate the diatom population of the whole flask. The counter, an amazing and expensive little machine, was triggered by the interruption of an electrical field each time a cell passed through a tiny constriction in a pipe. It was linked to a computer that sorted out the electronic pulses and broke them down according to the size of the tiny particles and displayed the results on the dimly glowing screen of an oscilloscope. To me the flickering, moving dots of light looked like a luminous, green snowstorm. A digital counter also showed the number of diatoms; the first count was 107,338 particles per 5 milliliters of solution.

Dr. O'Connors and his assistant agreed that this count didn't look right. The solution was too concentrated, which meant that more than one diatom at a time was being sucked through the counter's orifice. The remedy: dilute the solution 50 percent with filtered seawater. After this step, the counter worked more slowly but, they said, more accurately.

Next, they set up filters through which they poured the culture, with a running critique from a senior SUNY biologist they had invited to drop by. The diatom-laden filters were set aside to dry under a heater. Later they would be ground up and analyzed for chlorophyll quantity. All this went on to an accompaniment of banter about who had swiped which piece of equipment from whom.

Dr. O'Connors was called away early, so I was unable to watch him carry this practice experiment to its conclusion. However, he told me that it would have to be repeated until he had every step down pat, and conducted several times to establish its statistical validity.

As planned, later phases of the experiment would examine how well the ash blocks held up when exposed to seawater and whether organisms such as seaweeds, mussels, and barnacles could colonize them. For this, sample blocks would have to be planted out in Long Island Sound, and data would be taken by scuba divers.

When not engaged in a special project like the NYS ERDA project just described, Dr. O'Connors is involved in another research project at Flax Pond with Dr. Charles Wurster (which will be described in another chapter). He then comes in at 7:30 or 8:00 A.M., warms up the particle counter, and goes out to Flax Pond to collect his samples for the day. He runs them through various kinds of analyses until midafternoon, when he does his clean-up chores. Working up the data often takes him until 6:00 or 7:00 at night.

When he has a teaching assignment, he gives two two-hour lectures a week, and after-class question-and-answer sessions usually stretch class duty out to five hours. It takes him about three hours to prepare the material for each lecture. And about an hour a day is devoted to conferring with his students who drop into the office. In 1976–77 he had twenty-five graduate students in his class, and the number was expected to increase.

After Dr. O'Connors left, I took the opportunity to chat with his colleague, Dr. Duedall. I had to wait some time, as Dr. Duedall had gone over to Brookhaven National Laboratory, about half an hour's drive from Stony Brook, where he and Dr. Dayal often go to use the specialized equipment and exchange ideas with the scientists.

Duedall's day had not begun well. He came in at 7:30 to find that the heat had gone off in his end of the building. The outside temperature may have been 10 degrees. By the time he had located the maintenance man and gotten the heat back on, nearly an hour had passed. He worked a research project, preparing standard solutions for X-ray fluorescence measurements of copepods and particulate matter, until midmorning, when he rendezvoused with the typist who was typing up the thesis of one of his students. Together, they proofread the thesis until about one o'clock. After a quick sandwich lunch, Dr. Duedall went off to Brookhaven with Dr. Dayal. On the way back, he stopped at the Stony Brook administration office to pick up his travel expenses for a forthcoming trip to a conference in Santa Barbara. As he quoted me that day's temperatures in southern California, his whole face lighted up with anticipation.

As we talked, Dr. Duedall had to answer the phone several times. I remarked that an oceanographer's day seemed to consist in large part of interruptions. That was so, he agreed, and explained that his own most productive times for writing up his work were evenings and weekends. Shortly after that, he had to leave.

Other scientists may spend their days differently, and other institutions may have different arrangements, but what I saw at Stony Brook seemed pretty typical of what I'd seen elsewhere.

6

The Research Vessel

A LABORATORY AT SEA

Marine scientist Maurice Ewing once pontificated that the real lab was aboard the ship; the buildings on shore were just places for housing data. While Ewing was exaggerating in his usual colorful fashion, a ship is essential for any marine-science institution that wants to do research. It has often been said that you cannot bring nature into the lab. Therefore, to see what happens under natural conditions, you must go out where the nature you want to examine is. To do this in most cases requires a ship. (Scientists from Lamont have spent weeks on drifting ice floes making physical and chemical measurements in the Arctic, but that is a very special case.)

Research vessels, or R/Vs, as they are called in marine-science publications, come in all sizes from a 12-foot outboard runabout to ships 250 feet long and even larger. The small boats are used for half-day collecting trips near the school, and it is usually students who use them. The large vessels are used for long research assignments and deep-sea work.

The larger the vessel, of course, the more room there is for scientists and equipment. Thus, more science gets done per day on a large vessel than on a small one—at least, if things are

R/V *Atlantis,* Woods Hole's first ocean-going research vessel, served the institution until World War II, when it was pressed into duty by the Navy to patrol coastal waters for enemy submarines.

Woods Hole Oceanographic Institution

properly organized. Another advantage is that a large vessel can carry more fuel and more supplies than a small one, thus making possible a longer voyage. Since a good deal of time is always spent in just getting the R/V out to the area of ocean to be investigated, anything that gives more actual working time is valuable. This is especially true now that inflation has driven the cost of operating a major research vessel up to a level of $3,000 to $10,000 a day.

A third advantage of a large ship is that it is much more stable. It rolls, pitches, and yaws much less than a small vessel. This makes it a better platform for lowering and recovering instruments and equipment. A current meter, piston corer, or dredge, dangling and swinging from the end of its cable as the ship tosses about, can all too easily smash against the side of the ship, or into a person on deck. A large ship is also better for laboratory work, since scientists and technicians do not have to contend with sloshing beakers of reagents or samples that slide wildly around the work table. The more stable the ship, the easier it is to make delicate adjustments on instruments or to perform operations like dissecting a tiny organism. Lastly, but by no means unimportantly, a stable ship means less risk of seasickness. Ridiculous as it sounds, seasickness is a major plague aboard oceanographic R/Vs and eats up a sizable chunk of time. Some oceanographers avoid going to sea at all costs because they get too seasick to work.

So far it would seem that an oceanographic institution would want to build the largest R/V possible. But here economic considerations invade the designers' dreams of grandeur. A ship longer than 200 feet just costs too much to build nowadays, so a compromise must be made between what the scientists want and what the budget has room for. There are other compromises to be made all along the line. For example, an oceanographic research vessel does not need to be speedy while it is at work. Dredging and trawling must be done at low speeds, and for other tasks, such as coring, the ship must hold as still as possible. So for much of its time at sea the ship can get by with a low-power engine, which also offers the great advantage of using less fuel. On the other hand, everyone agrees that it is desirable for the ship to get from port to working area quickly, in order not to waste costly time in unproductive travel. It is also important to move quickly from station to station (a station is the spot where the ship gathers its data). The designer must then figure out the best balance between cost and performance. His work is made even harder by the fact that prices for everything are constantly rising—not only that, they don't rise at an even rate.

Then there is the problem of how to divide up the ship's interior space. A certain amount of room must go to the engine and other mechanical equipment. A certain amount must go to the galley and food lockers. But the comfort of the crew and the scientific party must also be considered, for discontented people do bad work. Crewmen, who spend a large part of the year at sea, should ideally have individual rooms where they can be away from everyone else at times. Otherwise, personal irritations may grow to serious proportions. How big should these rooms be? (On most vessels, the crewmen double up, and on Lamont's *Vema* they sleep in an old-fashioned fo'c's'le.) Scientists, who spend no more than a month on a cruise, customarily double up. But they, too, need a certain amount of elbow room in their tiny cabins.

How many showers and toilets are needed so that people don't have to wait in line to use them? A recreation room is necessary; how big must it be to accommodate the maximum number of people likely to crowd into it? Each square foot of space given over to one use means that much less space for any other use, and space on shipboard is a finite quantity.

Who pays for all of this? Very few institutions can afford the price of a research vessel. Most are paid for by government funds and owned by the National Science Foundation (NSF) or the Office of Naval Research. They are more or less on permanent loan to the institutions that operate them. The institutions must somehow scrounge up the money to pay for their maintenance and operation. Most of this money, like most of the other sources of income, comes from government grants and contracts. To use a homely metaphor, it comes from the same barrel but flows through a different spigot.

There are exceptions. Woods Hole owns outright the 210-foot oceangoing *Atlantis* II and the 40-foot coastal R/V *Asterias*. The University of Delaware owns its brand-new *Cape Henlopen*. Scripps owns three of its five active R/Vs; Lamont owns *Vema* and *Robert D. Conrad,* and so on. There are certain advantages to owning your own research vessel. You decide where it goes and when, and you decide who goes on it. You also do not have to worry about the Navy's or the NSF's telling you that the vessel is going to be laid up next year, although you must still somehow find the money to operate it. But owning one's own expensive R/V is not the rule.

If you have an oceanographic research vessel, you want to keep it as busy as possible. When it is tied up at the pier, it is not producing scientific data, and it costs plenty to keep even when it is not running. Lamont's vessels lead the fleet in sea time, logging an average of 100,000 miles of travel a year between them, and spending over three hundred days away from port. Lamont manages this by scheduling chiefly projects that take at least four to six months. Some institutions use stratagems like the following: Schedule a 4-week research voyage that ends in a West African port. Unload the scientists and their paraphernalia. (The scientists will fly home; the rest of the stuff will follow by air freight or ship.) Pick up a new party of scientists, perhaps with an entirely different objective, load on their gear, and chug off to a new station. Most institutions, however, bring their vessels home after three to five weeks at sea.

Despite the impression given by Cousteau films, life on a research vessel is mostly routine and hard work.* At times everyone must work around the clock to gather specimens and do analyses. This, of course, affects the quality of the work, but at least the samples are gotten on board. The major part of the analyses are done back on shore in any case, so that shipboard errors are not as serious as they might otherwise be. But errors do happen occasionally. Cores are dropped and shattered; wrong counts are taken of plankton samples; reagent solutions are mixed wrong, and so on. This is a regrettable fact of lab work, and scientists and technicians try to take it in stride. Results are checked as a routine step, and if errors are found, the work is done over.

The working day is long—twelve hours is the standard shift, and if there is a lot of material to be analyzed, the work goes on until it is done. On short cruises, it is not uncommon for everyone to work twenty hours at a stretch.

Two people share command of a research cruise: the chief scientist and the captain of the vessel. The chief scientist plans the cruise and lays out its objectives, decides how many scientists and how many technicians are to go, wheedles the necessary funds, puts in requisitions for supplies and equipment, and fills out endless forms. He also rides herd on the scientific party while at sea, doing his best to make sure that the assigned tasks get carried out properly. When scientists quarrel over whose work should have priority, it is the chief scientist who tries to smooth things out. If he has a temperamental person to deal with, this can be difficult. Nevertheless, the chief scientist still has the power to assign priorities. He also sees to it that the preliminary reports on the cruise get written up (no reports mean no money next time around) and assembles them into one coherent body of facts and figures. And it is he who decides where the bottom sampling, plankton netting, and other data gathering will be done.

---

*Cousteau's films dramatize only the highlights. The many hours of planning, preparation, and unavoidable drudgery that his teams put in are not shown.

But the chief scientist yields to the captain in all matters concerning the actual operation and safety of the vessel. The captain, usually a retired Navy or Coast Guard man, plans the course of the ship, determines how fast it will travel, and so on. He also makes the decision to cut the cruise short if safety requires it. This is probably the only real area of disagreement between captains and chief scientists. For example, the captain may receive a weather report that a violent storm is approaching. The scientists, who know that they will probably not get another chance to gather material at sea for at least a year, press the captain to stay on station and take a chance that the storm won't be too bad when it arrives. The captain, however, does not want to risk lives and his costly vessel, so he gives orders to bring in all collecting gear and sails off with a shipload of complaining scientists.

Some oceanographers love being at sea, but by no means all of them share this enthusiasm. A good many avoid cruises as much as possible, and some never go to sea but spend their careers ashore in the relative comfort of a laboratory, analyzing data and materials that someone else has collected. It is not just the physical discomfort of life on a small, crowded ship that makes them shun sea duty. The psychological factors are more important. There is the stress of working long hours under pressure to produce results. There are the inevitable frictions and personality clashes, magnified by having to live at very close quarters with other people with whom they must share quarters, toilets, and showers. More than one person has told me of the tensions that erupt around the two-week mark of a voyage.

But a research voyage is not all drudgery, tension, and hostilities. Scientists, techs, and crewmen do find time to relax during their free hours. There are bull sessions in the galley and the rec room; there are card games; if there are enough women on board, there may even be an occasional dance. The rec room also has a small but well-stocked library and a TV that plays movie and program cassettes. Some people bring along their own tape decks, guitars, and other instruments for solitary entertainment.

Although beer, wine, and liquor are forbidden on board an R/V, some is always smuggled aboard for discreet parties. The crewmen are not invited because of the danger of having an intoxicated man on watch; therefore it is essential to keep the celebration quiet so as not to rub it in. There is a good deal of off-duty socialization between scientists and technicians, but usually little between the scientific party and the crew, although this varies from ship to ship. On many vessels there is a traditional Hump Day party to mark the midpoint of the cruise. From there on, every day brings the ship closer to port.

Accommodations range from the spartan to the comfortable. The University of Connecticut's 65-foot *T-441,* for example, houses a total of eight people in a crowded bunkroom under the foredeck. The tiny galley looks barely adequate for preparing sandwiches. However, since the *T-441* seldom goes out for more than three or four days, no grave problems arise. The ship, a World War II cargo carrier, used to cross the Pacific with supplies for American attack forces. It is still in good shape, attentively maintained by its proud skipper, himself a Navy veteran.

On the other end of the spectrum are the new vessels, like the University of Rhode Island's *Endeavor,* Woods Hole's *Oceanus,* and Oregon State's *Wecoma.* These ships have two-man cabins for the scientists, a recreation room, and even sports equipment for those who crave exercise. Bunks are comfortable, and cruise members are encouraged to fix up their cabins to suit their own tastes.

Scientists spend a great deal of time on the R/V's of other institutions. A scientist's own institution may not be planning a cruise to the geographical area where he wants to work, or his specialty may not be represented. By making space available to scientists from other institutions, each institution gains a great deal of flexibility for its own people. Another benefit of this system is that scientists from different institutions are brought together; they exchange ideas, and it tends to keep them from getting ingrown.

Getting space on a research vessel is not as simple as it might seem. Let's take the case of a fictitious scientist, Bob Buchanan. Dr. Buchanan has successfully completed the first step of all and has gotten his project funded. Next, he must present it at the fall meeting of his institution, where all the scientists present their plans for the season two years ahead. Dr. Buchanan, a chemical oceanographer, wants to study the fate of oil spills in the northern reaches of the Atlantic Ocean. His colleagues have plans for projects off the mouth of the Orinoco River in South America, and the majority prevails. It is impossible for Dr. Buchanan to modify his project, because he specifically wants to investigate what happens to oil in cold water and cold air. However, he is not completely out of luck, because there is an organization called UNOLS (University-National Oceanographic Laboratory System) that acts as a clearinghouse to match scientists with ships. Bob Buchanan gets in touch with UNOLS and is assigned a slot on a research vessel from, let us say, the University of Rhode Island, which is scheduled for a research voyage in the North Atlantic at the time when he will be free to go.

It is not only the scientist who is unhappy if he can't get space on his own institution's ship. The institution is unhappy too, because efficiency drops for each space that is unfilled. And so the UNOLS office, housed at Woods Hole Oceanographic Institution, is kept busy with calls from scientists who need a vessel and institutions with vacancies crying to be filled. (This scenario is oversimplified, for all oceanographic institutions make a practice of reserving a certain proportion of spaces for researchers from other institutions.)

It sometimes happens that a scientist has to cancel his plans unexpectedly, and there is a last-minute vacancy on a research vessel. Then Chief Scientist X may make a hurried call to his old friend Department Head Y at another institution to ask if he has anyone he wants to send along. Such "piggybacking" scientists are sometimes disappointed, because their projects get last priority on the voyage.

Not all research cruises have room for all the specialties of oceanography. There are two philosophies of running a cruise. One, espoused by Maurice Ewing, is to gather as much of as many kinds of data as is humanly possible: physical, biological, geological, and chemical. The other approach is to limit the cruise to one field, or two closely related ones, so that there will be no conflict of objectives. There will be no flare-ups because the biologists want to steam around trawling for mid-depth organisms while the geologists want to sit still and take cores.

It is hard to say which system is more productive, but it is certain that oceanography would be far poorer without research vessels.

7

Woods Hole Oceanographic Institution

THE EAST-COAST TITAN

At the southern extremity of the "shoulder" of Cape Cod lies the little community of Woods Hole, Massachusetts, known to millions of travelers as the place where you catch the ferries for Nantucket and Martha's Vineyard. From Memorial Day to Labor Day, traffic jams the two-lane road to the ferry landing. A surprising number of visitors pass through without noticing the marine-research complex that makes Woods Hole one of the world's leading centers of marine science.

Woods Hole is the home of no fewer than four marine-science institutions. They are, in order of seniority, the Northeast Fisheries Center, the Marine Biological Laboratory, Woods Hole Oceanographic Institution, and the U.S. Geological Survey. The Fisheries Center is a shrine for summer tourists—its small but well-stocked aquarium is an excellent place to spend some of the interminable hours waiting for the ferry. But the one whose name rings a bell when you mention "oceanography" is the Woods Hole Oceanographic Institution, usually abbreviated in the profession to WHOI.

Members of rival institutions, perhaps with a touch of envious malice, sometimes pronounce this acronym as "Hooey." Around Woods Hole it is called "the Oceanographic." By any name,

Woods Hole Oceanographic Institution is one of the big two in American oceanography, as well as a leader on the world scene.

WHOI was established in 1930 with a $3 million grant from the Rockefeller Foundation. For some months the staff consisted only of the newly appointed director, Dr. Henry Bigelow, his secretary, Virginia Walker, and his general assistant, Columbus O'Donnell Iselin. Iselin was later to play an important part in WHOI's vital work for the Navy during World War II, and in 1950 he succeeded Bigelow as director. Bigelow himself was a Harvard-trained zoologist and disciple of Alexander Agassiz, the son of Louis Agassiz, whose short-lived summer school was the forerunner of the short-lived summer school on Penikese Island. One of Bigelow's first major tasks as a young Ph.D. had been to describe and classify the throngs of jellyfish he had helped to collect on Agassiz' expeditions in the early 1900's. As an independent investigator, he concentrated on a limited area of the Gulf of Maine, where he conducted pioneering studies on the fish, plankton, and hydrography. By the time Bigelow died in 1968, he had seen his institution go through a complete transformation.

One of Bigelow's first decisions as director of WHOI was to acquire a proper research vessel. He settled on a steel-hulled sailing ketch with an auxiliary engine, not only because many of his backers were wealthy yachtsmen but because a sailing ship was less dependent on fuel and was thought to be more stable than a steamer. (At that time steam was still the major source of power for ships.) The versatile Iselin was appointed master of the vessel while it was still under construction.

Money was available in 1930 for research projects, but neither buildings nor ship was ready. Rather than spend an unproductive summer, Bigelow and the trustees decided to contribute some of the idle funds to Sir Hubert Wilkins's daringly planned and highly unconventional Arctic expedition. Wilkins's idea was to use a submarine to take echo soundings, samples of ice, water, sediments, and plankton, and other measurements beneath the polar ice cap. The U.S. Navy was interested enough to lend the British explorer a worn-out submarine that Wilkins rigged out with his scientific equipment and renamed the *Nautilus,* after Jules Verne's fictional craft. Wilkins's concept was sound, but the sub he had to work with was not, and mechanical troubles almost aborted the expedition. Losing its diving planes at the edge of the Arctic ice pack, the *Nautilus* was unable to go beneath the ice. A week and a half of surface work was all that was possible before the oncoming Arctic winter forced the damaged sub to turn back. However, enough data were gathered for WHOI to publish three papers as its first contribution to science. One of the authors of these papers was the Norwegian meteorologist Harald Sverdrup, who later became the director of Scripps Institution of Oceanography.

By the following summer, 1931, the new Woods Hole laboratory was ready, and Bigelow began the long task of recruiting and training a staff of researchers. At the time, there were only about a hundred oceanographers in the United States, and most of them already had commitments. During the 1930's, WHOI operated as a summer institution, staffed mainly by visiting scientists and graduate students from universities around the country. Not until World War II did WHOI shift to year-round operation, and not until the late 1960's did the institution formally take on the mission of teaching as well as research. Today WHOI not only grants Ph.D.s in its own right but also has a joint program with MIT in oceanography and ocean engineering. It also has cross-registration programs with Harvard, Yale, and Brown. To accommodate its expanded programs, WHOI built a brand new, ultramodern facility, the Clark Laboratory (completed 1973), on the nearby Quissett Campus just outside the village.

During World War II WHOI became a frantically busy center of research for the Navy. Not only did the Woods Hole oceanographers train submarine commanders in the art of hiding under the

Preparing to lower a set of physical oceanographic instruments from the A-frame at the stern of a Woods Hole research vessel. This instrument package measures fine gradations of ocean, temperature, pressure, and salinity.
Woods Hole Oceanographic Institution

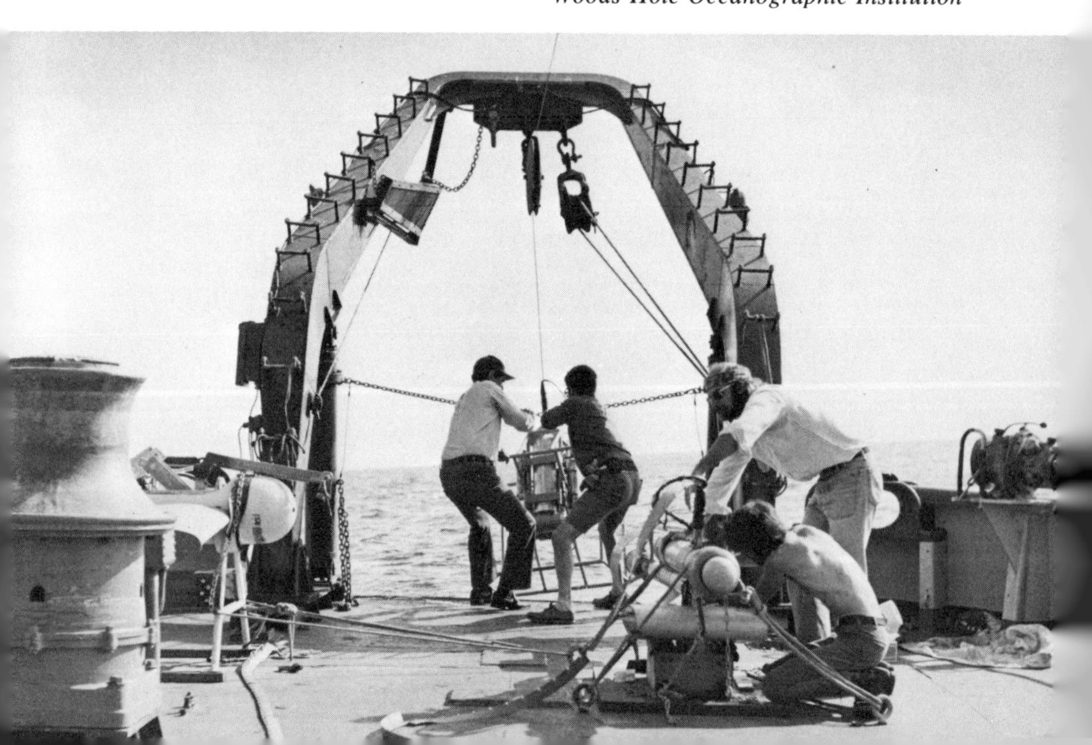

thermocline and delve into the effects of temperature and salinity on sonar; they mapped currents and seafloors; they investigated underwater explosives; and they devised ways to slow down the fouling of ships' bottoms by barnacles and other sea life. The antifouling program was so successful that the Navy credited it with saving 10 percent of the Navy's fuel bill—less fouling means less drag. And the Navy went on to sponsor a high proportion of WHOI's postwar research.

Bigelow had always been a blue-water oceanographer, interested in studying the open sea and its life, and his successors continued this policy. One of WHOI's preeminent specialties has been a continuing study of the Gulf Stream and, in the 1970's, of its eddies. In recent years the Oceanographic has expanded into such areas of worldwide concern as pollution studies and coastal-zone ecology, but it is still regarded as a deep-water institution.

One current project is about as deep-water as you can get—to find safe disposal sites for radioactive wastes from nuclear power plants and from the military in the floors of the deep ocean basins. Radioactivity is not the only danger posed by these wastes. Some of the substances in them are highly poisonous as well. Plutonium, for instance, remains extremely dangerous for nearly half a million years. Dry land is not a suitable place to dispose of these wastes. Even the most durable containers would corrode away long before their contents had lost enough radioactivity to become harmless, and the wastes would slowly leach into the groundwater, endangering people and animals who drank the water and getting into the food web. There is also the distinctly unpleasant possibility that terrorists could seize radioactive wastes and use them to blackmail the world into submission.

The other alternative is the seabed, and a WHOI scientist, Charles Hollister, began investigating this possibility in 1973. At one point it was thought that oceanic trenches would be the ideal spots. The trenches are formed where the slowly moving plates of the Earth's crust push against each other and one slowly glides down into the molten depths of the mantle. Anything buried deep in the descending rim of a plate could inexorably be carried down with it, as if by a gigantic conveyor belt into the Earth's interior, and not emerge again for incalculable periods of time. However, geological oceanographers found that a good deal of volcanic and earthquake activity occurs along the trenches of the ocean, and there is a strong possibility that radioactive waste buried in a trench might be tossed up into the ocean or the atmosphere all too soon. In addition, the trenches are usually near continents and thus close to human populations. Hollister and his colleagues concluded that the safest place to dispose of the nuclear-waste canisters would be in the middle of a plate, where the risk of a volcanic eruption is microscopically small, and in the middle of one of the biologically unproductive circular currents called gyres, so that even if waste did escape into the water, it would be held back from entering the food web.

As now envisioned, the wastes from nuclear reactors would be dried out and then fused with glass, which would protect them from moisture and leaching. The glass would be put into metal canisters, which would then be sunk deep into the sediment of the ocean floor. Much more research is needed before seafloor disposal of these perilous wastes becomes a reality. Meanwhile, they continue to pile up on land.

A project with less ominous overtones is FAMOUS (French-American Mid-Ocean Undersea Study), a geological study that took three submersibles down to investigate a section of the Mid-Atlantic Ridge. Much had been learned about the ridge by means of echo sounding, seismic profiling, and other remote sensing techniques, and by drilling and random sampling from surface ships. But certain fundamental questions remained unanswered. Why was the ridge a center of mini-earthquakes? What were the geophysical processes at work along the ridge? Were minerals being deposited there from fissures in the seafloor? It became clear that these questions could be answered only through firsthand observation by trained scientists, and that the only way to get scientists down to the seafloor was to have them dive down in submersibles.

Planning for FAMOUS began in 1971. From the outset it was a joint project, involving scientists and ships from four nations and from many institutions. France contributed the bathyscaphe *Archimède,* which is able to dive to 36,000 feet, and the newly built diving saucer *Cyana,* with a depth capability of 10,000 feet. The United States sent *Alvin,* based at WHOI and operated by the institution. Originally designed for dives to 6,000 feet, Alvin was refitted with a new pressure hull of titanium-steel alloy able to stand the pressure of 12,000 feet of water. The area to be studied was the great rift that runs down the center of the ridge; in the region selected, it lay from 8,000 to 10,000 feet below sea level.

The leader of the American team was James Heirtzler of Woods Hole Oceanographic Institution. Dr. Heirtzler told me something of the tremendous preparation that went into making FAMOUS a success. The area had to be thoroughly surveyed in advance to choose safe diving sites. Practice dives had to be made to get the routines down letter-perfect. French and American scientists had to work together on all sorts of tasks to overcome the language

Ready for a dive, *Alvin* waits on the deck of *Lulu*. In foreground are the submersible's mechanical arm and a wire basket for specimens collected with the aid of the arm.

Woods Hole Oceanographic Institution

barrier. This was more than just the difference between French and English. The Frenchmen used quite a different set of terms not only for diving but also for geology. They also held different theories about the origins of geological features. All these differences had to be ironed out so that the co-workers could understand each other.

The survey began in 1972 with a detailed remapping of the seafloor. Britain and Canada took part in this phase along with the United States and France. One of the star pieces of equipment was Britain's mighty 7-ton, deep-towed side-scanning sonar, named GLORIA. Large sections of the bottom were photographed with a newly developed wide-view underwater camera. Seismic and magnetic studies gave evidence of the kinds of rock that formed the rift valley. Heat-flow measurements often gave clues to where the magma lay closest to the surface.

The surface explorations continued through the summer of 1973, and the *Archimède* made several dives into the rift. But the real year of the submersibles was 1974. *Alvin* made seventeen dives, and the French submersibles made twenty-seven. Each diving site had been chosen with extreme care. It could have no strong currents—submersibles are feebly powered, and a strong current could dash them against rocks. Unstable rock formations

The French bathyscaphe *Archimède* can descend to depths of more than 36,000 feet. It played a vital role in exploring the Mid-Atlantic Rift in Project FAMOUS.
CNEXO

were also avoided, as they could collapse and bury a submersible beyond hope of recovery. Epicenters of earthquake activity had been located by sensitive seafloor seismometers, and the subs avoided these areas. They were very cautious about approaching areas where they might encounter an undersea volcanic eruption.

For the scientists, the chance to visit the seafloor was a truly exciting experience. They saw with their own eyes phenomena that they would otherwise never have observed. Thanks to skillful pilots, the dives were smooth and uneventful. As Dr. Heirtzler described it, a dive was like an hour-long elevator ride to the seafloor. Once there, the experience was like a pleasant nature walk as the little sub cruised along at 1 mph a few feet above the bottom. *Alvin* could maneuver like a butterfly, Dr. Heirtzler reminisced, and you could look at whatever you wanted, from any angle. The three large viewports gave excellent visibility, and the scientists spoke all their observations and impressions into tape recorders as they floated past the quiet, moonlike undersea landscape. When each dive was completed, the scientists were immediately "debriefed" by their colleagues who had not gone down, so that they could get the divers' impressions while they were fresh.

Of course, not everything was entrusted to verbal reports. On each dive, about 3,000 photographs were taken to provide visual evidence. Samples of rock and water were taken with *Alvin*'s remote-controlled mechanical claw and other devices and stored in a "lazy susan" basket under the vessel's nose. Actual bottom time ran from five to eight hours, and the routine was meticulously preplanned to avoid wasting costly time in random searching for something interesting. (*Alvin* cost $4,000 per day to operate, and the research vessel that had to accompany it cost another $4,000, so that useful diving time averaged over $1,000 per hour.) Sonar beacons on the bottom guided the sub precisely around each dive location.

As Dr. Heirtzler put it, "On an expedition like this you're delighted to find little surprises, but you don't want to find big surprises because that means you haven't done your homework." In spite of all the homework the scientists of FAMOUS had done, they did find some big surprises. One was the topography of the rift itself. They found that the western wall was quite different from the eastern wall, being much steeper and containing different types of rock formations. They were also surprised to find zones filled with fissures in the bedrock, from a few inches to yards wide, evidence of the titanic forces wrenching the Earth's crust. Perhaps the biggest surprise was the existence of a narrow line of hills running down the middle of the rift valley, where all

Shepherded by two wet-suited, flippered divers, *Alvin* returns to *Lulu* after a successful trip to the depths.

Woods Hole Oceanographic Institution

the volcanic action takes place. The scientists also found evidence that the rift's volcanic activity was not continuous, but occurred on a nearly 10,000-year cycle.

Project FAMOUS was so successful that similar projects were planned for other parts of the ocean. In early 1977, for example, *Alvin* made a series of dives on the crest of the Galapagos Rift, in the eastern Pacific, to look for hot springs that emit metal-rich water. A surprising discovery was that the areas right around some of the springs are full of life—ten-inch clams, mussels, crabs, sea anemones, and a variety of other species. The scientists theorized that specialized bacteria, which live on hydrogen sulfide in the water, are the basis of this food web.

Another international project in which WHOI took a leading part is GEOSECS (Geochemical Ocean Sections Study). The major objective of GEOSECS was to understand the origin and circulation of the deep water in the oceans. According to Dr. Derek Spencer, chairman of WHOI's Department of Chemistry, the idea was proposed at a summer conference on geophysical fluid dynamics by MIT's Henry Stommel, who suggested using radioactive elements to trace the deep ocean currents. This is a delicate and tricky procedure, since the concentration of radioactive elements in the ocean is extremely low, even when augmented by fallout and nuclear-power-plant waste. However, recently developed technology made it possible.

Dr. Derek Spencer (standing) watches the instrument panel in one of the *Knorr*'s four shipboard laboratories during the far-reaching GEOSECS project.
Woods Hole Oceanographic Institution

As Dr. Spencer explained patiently to me, the GEOSECS investigators relied principally on carbon-14, radium-226, and radium-228, all of which occur naturally. C-14 enters the seawater from the atmosphere; Ra-226 and Ra-228 enter it from the bottom sediments, as products of the decay of naturally occurring uranium-238. They make convenient time clocks: C-14 has a half-life of 5,700 years; Ra-226 has a half-life of 1,600 years, and Ra-228 one of a mere 5 years. Thus by measuring their concentration in a parcel of water a chemical oceanographer could tell where that water originated and how fast it had traveled from its point of origin. But in order to use these radioactive time clocks, the scientists first had to learn the rate at which they entered the water.

It turned out that they had to measure fifty-nine properties of each tracer element, including their interactions with other substances present in ocean water. They had to compare them with stable chemical analogs and go through a mountain of calculations that only a scientist could follow. Much of the analytical work was done on board ship, often involving 1,000-liter water samples (about 264 gallons). A new device, the remote-controlled rosette sampler, was of great help to the scientists. This consists of a central core that contains salinity, pressure, and temperature sensors. The sensors constantly send measurements back to a shipboard computer via a conducting cable, and the computer instantly calculates the depth as the core is lowered or raised. Around the core are strapped a dozen or so sampling bottles, and at any given depth the scientists can close them one by one with an electrical signal. The advantage of this method over older ones is that it gives precise depth control, whereas with a string of Nansen or Nisken bottles you are never sure of the true depth of the bottles' contents because currents may carry the cable out of the vertical plane. Said Dr. Spencer, "For the first time we had eyes in the ocean."

Work at sea began for GEOSECS in 1971, lasting into 1978. Sampling for the Atlantic and Pacific Oceans was completed in 1974; the Indian Ocean sampling winding up in 1978. One of the discoveries made by the participating scientists concerned the deep-water layer. Most of the deep water of the world's oceans originates in the North Atlantic around Iceland. (The Antarctic contributes a relatively small portion of the deep water.) The

Rosette water sampler similar to this one played important roles in GEOSECS
Woods Hole Oceanographic Institution

GEOSECS investigators found that this deep-water layer is being renewed much more rapidly than was previously supposed. Moreover, the deep Arctic water is not produced at a continuous rate. For years little may be produced; then a great gush of extremely dense, cold water comes down from the north. For a parcel of water to travel from the North Atlantic to the Antarctic and be carried around and up into the North Pacific takes about 1,000 years.

It was known that ocean water mixes much faster horizontally than vertically—about 1 million times as fast. The GEOSECS scientists have shown that this affects the way in which chemicals may be removed from the water, which is important in understanding how rapidly any waste material introduced into the ocean disperses and where it will go. Another valuable spin-off was the first set of consistently good measurements of nutrients in the world ocean, mapped vertically as well as horizontally. This information is useful to scientists concerned with biological productivity, for it tells them how much life can exist in a given area of the sea and how much more life could be supported in certain areas if the water were enriched by, say, artifically induced upwelling.

Physical oceanographer Mel Briscoe works on a somewhat more modest scale, studying internal waves. Dr. Briscoe must be an excellent teacher, for he held me spellbound as he explained what is known about these gigantic perturbations of the water. And they are truly gigantic, sometimes measuring hundreds of meters in height and tens of miles from crest to crest.

Internal waves, he told me, were first described by Benjamin Franklin in 1762. On one of his official voyages to England, bad weather kept Franklin confined to his cabin most of the time. To light up the dark little cubbyhole, he devised a hanging lamp made from a glass tumbler. The bottom third of the tumbler was filled with water; the middle third was filled with lamp oil; on top of this floated a cork that held the wick. As the ship pitched and rolled, Franklin noticed waves forming where the oil and water met. This surprised him because he had performed experiments at sea in which oil poured on stormy waters calmed the waves.

Internal waves are of more than theoretical interest. They affect the surface of the water and produce a mysterious drag on ships, known as "dead water." They also pose a serious threat to submarines. Invisible and undetectable by sonar, they can carry a submarine down past its depth limit, and the luckless vessel is crushed. It is thought that the U.S. submarine *Thresher,* sunk on a test run off Cape Cod, may have been carried to its doom by an internal wave.

The first person to observe internal waves in the sea was the Norwegian explorer Fridtjof Nansen, in 1893, when his ship was caught in dead water sailing out of a fjord. However, the phenomenon of dead water was not analyzed until 1906, by the Swedish oceanographer Vagn Walfrid Ekman. In the 1930's oceanographers began to investigate the causes of internal waves, but the era of modern understanding did not begin until 1970.

Internal waves form at the interface where two fluids of slightly different densities meet. An example is the colored oil and water of the popular "ocean in a bottle," or the oil and water in Franklin's lamp. Internal waves can also form in a single fluid where there are layers of different densities, as in the ocean, which is slightly denser in the deeper waters than near the surface. They do not form at the surface of the ocean, because air and water have such different densities (water is roughly 900 times as heavy as air), but they do form underneath the surface where water masses of different densities meet but mingle only slightly.

For years, Mel Briscoe explained, physical oceanographers searched for *the* cause of internal waves. Some believed they were caused by currents, while others thought they were caused by winds or tides. Today's thinking is that all of these factors are probably involved.

How do they act to produce internal waves? Basically, what happens is that some force acts to raise a parcel of water slightly. It is now a little bit heavier than the water surrounding it, and it sinks. Inertia carries it down beyond its original position, and it is suddenly lighter than the water around it, so it bobs up. The up-and-down cycle is repeated many times and, like tossing a stone into a pond, creates waves. Each internal wave has its own unique wavelength and frequency, varying from a few minutes to a day or so. Early measurements did not last long enough to get a good picture; they picked up only a few cycles. Modern internal-wave measurements last at least a month and preferably several months. The waves are measured by flow meters strung out along a cable supported by a buoy at the top end and tethered to the seafloor at the other end. The Buoy Group at WHOI has developed automatically recording flow meters that can function as deep as 6,000 meters (almost four miles) and stay out for a year.

Internal waves occur at every depth beneath the surface and in all parts of the ocean. Mel Briscoe thinks they play an important part in the mixing of water masses. He was slated to learn more about this on a JASIN (Joint Air-Sea Interaction) cruise in 1978.

Biologist John Teal has studied the Sargasso Sea as an ecosystem (he and his wife have written an excellent book on it) and has investigated transoceanic bird migration. But his major lifework

On board the R/V Knorr, scientists and students make ready to attach a current meter to its mooring. The ribbed plastic spheres enclose hollow, buoyant glass floats to hold the meter vertical in the water.

Benthos, Inc.

is the ecology of salt marshes, those fragile zones that serve as nurseries for so much of our marine life. At Woods Hole he has conducted a series of studies at the nearby Great Sippewissett Marsh, with colleagues from Boston University and the Marine Biological Laboratory, to ascertain how manipulating the environment in various ways affects the productivity of the marsh. Another goal of the experiments was to learn whether the marsh could serve to purify sewage wastes.

Accordingly, they laid out small plots, about two thirds the size of a basketball court. Some of these were treated with commercial fertilizer made of sewage sludge (the processing of the sludge kills disease organisms), and others were fertilized with urea (a nitrogen compound) or phosphate to act as controls and to see what effects nitrogen and phosphorus had by themselves. They measured such changes as increase in the growth of the grass, increase in protein content, and changes in the numbers of insects and other animals.

Dr. Teal found that the sewage sludge increased the productivity of the marsh significantly, as did the nitrogen fertilizer. (The phosphate did very little for it.) The grass grew taller, lusher, and more nutritious, and it yielded a bountiful harvest of detritus. Detritus is the basic substance in the food web of a salt marsh. It is composed of the partially decayed remains of plants and the bacteria that feed busily on them. The bacteria are eaten by all kinds of tiny organisms that in turn become food for larger animals all the way up the food web to such big predators as fish, blue herons, and raccoons.

The heavy metals present in the sewage sludge caused no observable ill effects. The only casualties were fiddler crabs and greenhead fly larvae, which were killed by dieldrin, a pesticide that was still being used and so was present in the sludge for the first few years of the experiment. Most people, Dr. Teal admitted, would regard the killing of greenhead flies as an unmixed blessing. However, he was concerned that it might have long-range effects on the marsh ecosystem, since the larvae are an important food for other marsh dwellers. This still remains to be studied. He and his colleagues also found that the marsh retained all the nitrogen that was fed to it. The nitrogen did not find its way into the sea to cause a choking population explosion of algae.

The implications of the experiment are twofold. Fertilization can increase the productivity of salt marshes and so in the long run boost the populations of commercial and sport fishes. Salt marshes may also serve to dispose of sewage productively, if the problem of disease organisms is licked.

Dr. John Ryther is tackling the sewage problem from another angle. In a corner of the Quissett Campus is his Environmental Systems Laboratory, which uses treated sewage as the basis for a complex aquacultural system of many species.

Dr. Ryther is attempting to duplicate natural food chains, and the system works as follows: The sewage first goes into ponds, where it is mixed with seawater and nourishes a thick population of algae. The algal soup is piped into tanks, where it is fed to edible shellfish such as oysters and clams. The shellfish wastes, high in nitrogen, nourish seaweeds, which can be harvested and treated to extract the valuable products carrageenan and agar, which are used in a host of products from ice cream to toothpaste, beer foam, and molds for false teeth. Alternatively, the seaweed can be fermented to yield methane gas for fuel or treated to yield synthetic petroleum. Sea worms also feed on the shellfish wastes, and these have been successfully fed to winter flounder, a popular food fish. Lobsters have been added to the tanks to feed on the worms and on the epiphytic animals, such as barnacles, that grow on the shellfish and the walls of the tanks. The lobsters so far have thrived on this diet and grown faster than normal.

There are other alternative pathways. The algae can be extracted, dried, and added to animal feed after suitable treatment. Or they can be fed to brine shrimp, which can either be marketed directly or used to feed fish on the premises. In every case there is a salable product.

Ryther's researchers ran into a problem: The algae that native East Coast oysters thrive on do not grow in the sewage ponds. Other, less nutritious species crowd them out. Taking the path of least resistance, the Ryther team searched for shellfish that would thrive on the algae that they were able to raise. They found three foreign species, the Japanese oyster, the Manila clam, and the European oyster, all delicacies in their native regions, that did exceedingly well. Only two things stand in the way of making the system a commercial success. One is the possible presence of disease organisms in the sewage—as yet there is no economical way of killing them without harming the shellfish too. The other is the heavy metal content of the sewage, which may build up in the shellfish to dangerous levels. Tom Losordo, the project manager, told me that another five to seven years of research would be required to solve these problems. However, he expected to see sewage-farm seaweed on the industrial market in another two years.

Dr. Ryther's scheme differs from other aquaculture programs in one important respect. The goal of ordinary aquaculture is to raise salable fish and shellfish. Everything else is a means to that end. Dr. Ryther's objective is to purify sewage by a biological method that yields the valuable by-product of seafood. The idea is that the profits from this by-product would pay in large part for the costs of sewage treatment, reducing the burden on the taxpayer. It is estimated that, under the Ryther system, fifty-one acres of ponds and tanks can handle the sewage of 11,000 people and yield an annual shellfish harvest of 1 million pounds; so one day communities along the shore may be cleaning up their sewage problems at a profit.

It would be difficult to discuss Woods Hole and the Oceanographic Institution without mentioning the Marine Biological Laboratory, which has played such an important part in the history of both. The Marine Biological Laboratory, MBL for short, was founded in 1888. Woods Hole was picked for the site because the U.S. Fish Commission was already operating a laboratory there, and because the marine fauna and flora were unusually varied and abundant in that area, thanks to the variety of environments (rocky shores, sand and mud flats, open coast, and sheltered inlets) and to the meeting nearby of the Gulf Stream and the cold Labrador Current.

The idea of the founders of the MBL was that certain life processes, such as cell division, muscle contraction, and the conduction of impulses by nerves, could be studied more easily and more cheaply in simple sea animals than in mammals. This idea was by no means radical, but in certain other ways the MBL was quite unconventional. It grew out of a summer institute set up at Annisquam, Massachusetts, by the Woman's Education Association of Boston, and from the very beginning it had women students and instructors working side by side with men. Women were also on the board of trustees from the start.

The MBL was also one of the few scientific institutions that welcomed Negroes, and the pioneer Negro physiologist E. E. Just did most of his work there.

The first director of the MBL, Charles Otis Whitman, had previously taught at the University of Tokyo, and the long tradition of contact with Japan was broken only by World War II. In 1975 Emperor Hirohito, in private life a marine biologist, took time off from a state visit to the United States to sneak a peek at some hydroids at the MBL. Hirohito's scientific papers on hydroid classifications fill a respectable shelf space at the MBL library, the finest of its kind in the world. With over 15,000 books

The faculty of the Marine Biological Laboratory in 1895, untypically for its time, included a woman.

Marine Biological Laboratory

and a collection of more than 5,200 periodicals, it is open twenty-four hours a day. Desk space in the stacks is a privilege coveted by researchers from many countries.

The MBL shares its library with Woods Hole Oceanographic Institution; in fact, the availability of the MBL library was one of the principal reasons for establishing WHOI in Woods Hole. And it was a director of the MBL, Frank Lillie, who first saw the need for an East Coast counterpart of Scripps and proposed the idea to the National Academy of Sciences. The NAS, in turn, passed on the idea to the Rockefeller Foundation, and the rest is history.

There has always been a close relationship between the two institutions and their scientists, although WHOI has worked mainly on broad oceanographic questions and the MBL has concentrated on specialized physiological research. The MBL's work has been extremely productive. Thirty Nobel Prize winners have worked there at some point in their careers—men such as Ivan Pavlov, the pioneer Russian psychologist, Selman Waksman, discoverer of streptomycin, Max Delbrück and Salvador Luria, who elucidated the reproductive mechanism of viruses, and James Watson, a codiscoverer of the structure of DNA. Others were Haldan K. Hartline and George Wald, who shared the prize in 1967 for their research in vision with Ragnar Granit, a Swede, and Albert Szent-Györgyi, famed for his work

The squid *Loligo pealei* is one of the chief experimental animals at the MBL. During the busy summer season, investigators at the MBL use as many as two hundred squid a day.

Linda Golder and Scrantz, Marine Biological Laboratory

A student dissects a squid to obtain one of its giant axons, or nerve fibers.
Marine Biological Laboratory

on vitamin C and on the biochemical mechanisms of muscle contraction (1937). Some did their prize-winning work at the MBL; others derived their inspirations there.

The Nobel laureates won fame with their contributions to mankind's welfare, but there were unsung heroes of the MBL, too—such humble experimental animals as the horseshoe crab, the dogfish, the sea urchin, and the squid. Each year some one hundred reseachers use about 12,000 squid in neurobiological investigations.

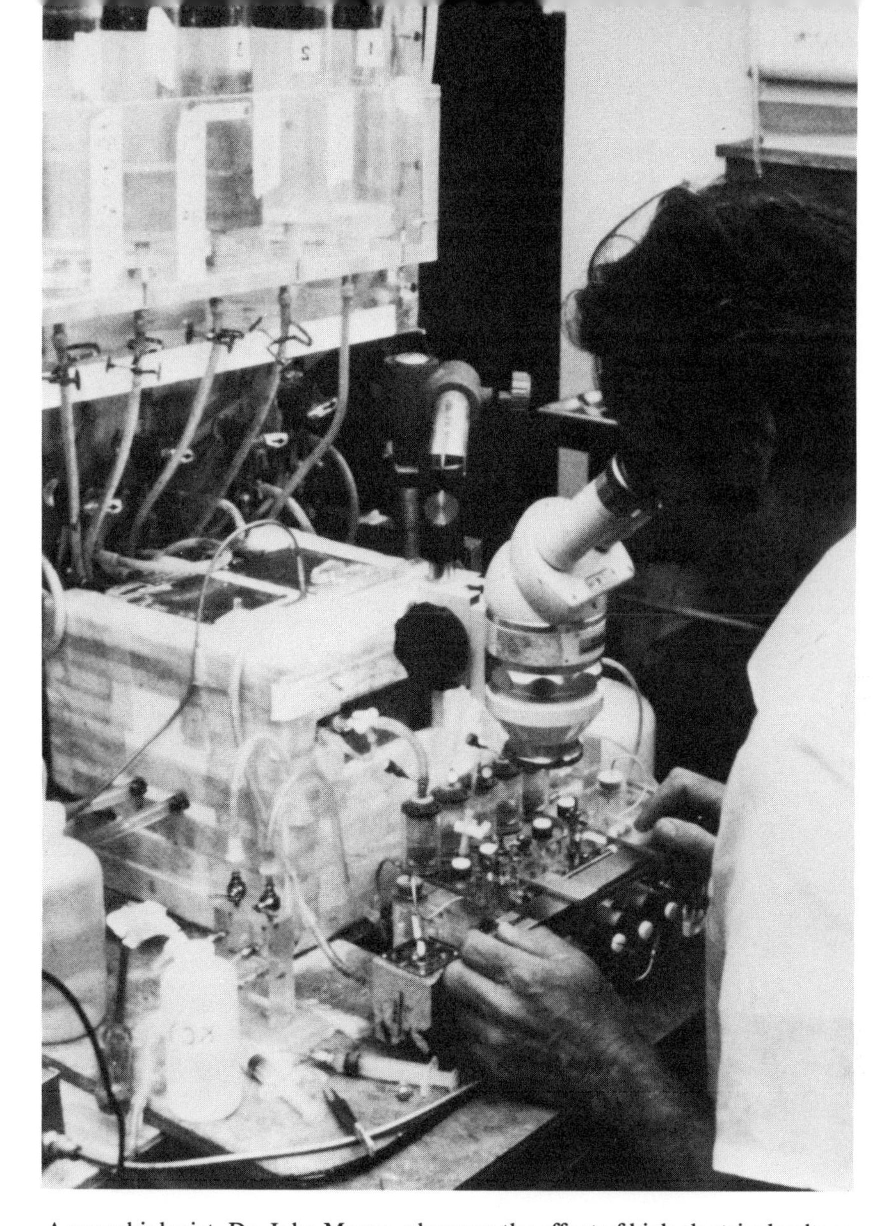

A neurobiologist, Dr. John Moore, observes the effect of high electrical voltage on squid axons. *Marine Biological Laboratory*

The MBL's use of squid in studies of the nervous system goes back to 1936, when a visiting English biologist, John Z. Young, cut up some local squids and found that each of the nerves in their mantles consisted of a single giant axon, or nerve fiber. So large were these fibers that electrodes could be inserted directly into them to study the way they conducted impulses. Young's discovery made it possible for another visiting English scientist, Alan L. Hodgkin, and MBL staffer Kenneth S. Cole to perform actual measurements of the currents generated by the nerves. By studying what happened when he applied different voltages to the squid axons, Cole laid much of the groundwork from which others brought to light the underlying mechanisms of nerve activity. For this work Cole was awarded the National Medal of Science in 1967 and in 1972 was made a member of Britain's prestigious Royal Society. (Honors in science come with maddening slowness.) Hodgkin, back in England, went on to develop a mathematical description of how these processes worked. Largely because of this work, he and his partner, Andrew F. Huxley, shared the Nobel Prize in 1963 with the Australian physiologist John Eccles.

The senior animal on the MBL's unsung-hero roster is unquestionably the sea urchin. Since the year the institution opened, the urchin's eggs and sperm have been used by cellular biologists to investigate such fundamental processes as how cell membranes function, how cells derive energy from respiration, and how the genes are "switched" on and off during the development of the embryo from the fertilized egg. Such research has been valuable in the understanding of cancer, and a promising new line of investigation may lead to a method of birth control in humans by immunizing women to an enzyme that aids the sperm to penetrate the egg wall.

Another of the "unsung heroes" of the MBL's work is the sea urchin. This blunt-spined urchin has been turned upside down to expose its tube feet.
Linda Golder and Scrantz, Marine Biological Laboratory

Around 1927 Hartline began his prize-winning studies on the visual system of that archaic sea-dwelling arthropod, the horseshoe crab. His students and followers have carried on the work for five decades, contributing much of what is known about photoreception and vision. More recently, scientists at the MBL have found that an extract of this animal's blue, copper-containing blood can be used as a chemical detector for certain dangerous bacterial toxins.

Scientists working with sponges were intrigued by the phenomenon of regeneration in these simple animals. If a living sponge is forced through a fine-meshed sieve, it is broken up into single cells and small clumps of cells. But if these cells are allowed to stand for a while, they regroup themselves into a new, perfectly functional sponge. If cells from two different species of sponge are mixed together, they somehow manage to sort themselves out. Recently MBL biologists began to analyze the physical and chemical features of the cell surfaces that allow these forcibly dissociated sponge cells to recognize each other and regroup. The results have contributed to our understanding of how cancer cells spread in the body and how the tissues and the organs of the fetus are formed during gestation.

Fishermen regard the goosefish (one of the angler fishes) as a repulsive pest. But MBL scientists discovered that its pancreas is peculiarly useful in diabetes research, because the isles of Langerhans—the portions of the pancreas that produce the hormone insulin—are separate from the rest of the gland, which synthesizes digestive enzymes. Insulin is the hormone that controls the burning of sugar in the body, and when the pancreas fails to synthesize it, the result is diabetes.

In addition to such traditional studies, the MBL has expanded into new fields; marine environmental biology, neurobiology, and the genetics of marine organisms. Researchers from the National Institute of Health, based in Bethesda, Maryland, are working on biophysics at the MBL.

For well over half a century the MBL was strictly a summer institute for research and teaching. Scientists from around the world would apply as early as November for work space in the labs or the library, and graduate students would apply for the intensive summer courses. Application was a highly competitive process, and not every scientist was accepted. Work began in June, and after Labor Day everyone departed en masse, save three or four researchers like Szent-Györgyi, who liked the solitude of the off-season. During the summer, the institution was one of the most sought-after gathering places for marine scientists; during the rest of the year it lay idle.

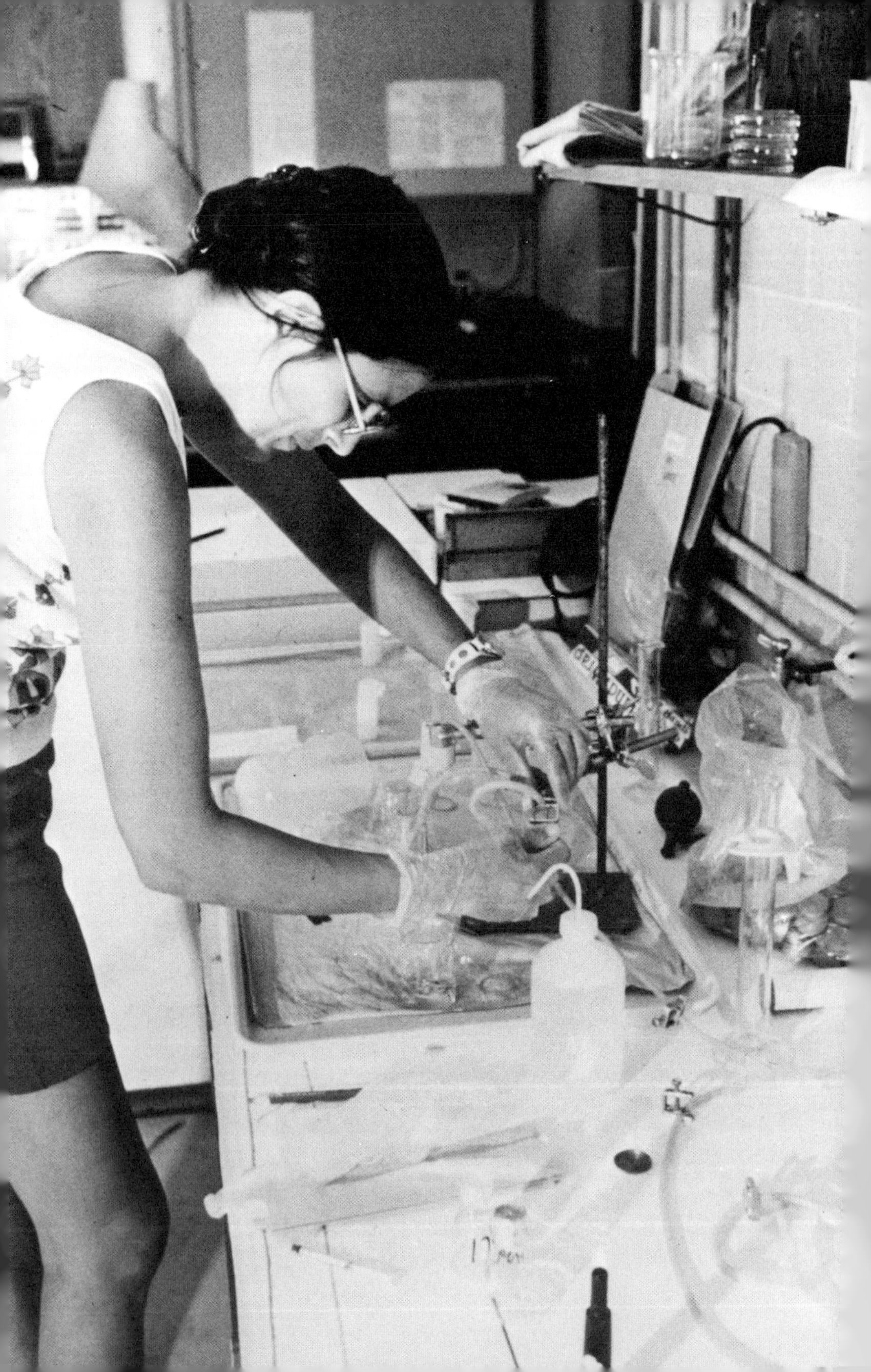

In the late 1960's, however, it became clear to the trustees of the MBL that summer operation was not bringing in enough revenue to support the research programs. And so the MBL gradually began to convert to year-round operation while holding fast to the best summer programs. One of its features is the popular January course for undergraduates, who earn credit at their own schools. The facilities are used at other times by groups of faculty and students from colleges and universities for short, intensive courses, such as the course in invertebrate zoology given by Temple University.

The Boston University Marine Program, known as BUMP, runs all year long. BUMP courses are open to students of the MBL and WHOI, and there is a lively interchange of ideas. Another year-round program is conducted by the MBL's Ecosystems Center, under the direction of Dr. George M. Woodwell. Operating under the philosophy that all parts of the biosphere are interrelated, the scientists of the Ecosystems Center investigate everything from salt-marsh ecology to population studies of large terrestrial mammals such as the African elephant, and their effects on the environment. A typical research project involved the real-estate development of the valley of the little North River, near Plymouth, Massachusetts.

A major ongoing project involves the carbon budget of the world: How much carbon is tied up in living matter? How much lies in organic remains such as oil and coal? How much is in the atmosphere? Where is the carbon going? One of the findings of this program is that the amount of carbon dioxide in the world's atmosphere is slowly but steadily increasing. The analyses suggest that deforestation and the growth of agriculture have contributed as much to the increase of CO_2 in the atmosphere as all the burning of coal and oil. Marshes have been found to be "sinks" for carbon. They affect the environment in another way by releasing hydrogen sulfide into the atmosphere as their organic matter decays. The malodorous gas is oxidized and reacts with water vapor in the air to form sulfuric acid. The result is acid rainfall. The ramifications of such research seem literally endless and will be increasingly important as man puts more and more stress on his environment.

Wearing plastic gloves for safety, this student at the MBL is working in the "hot lab," performing radioactive labeling of plant materials for a course in experimental botany.

Marine Biological Laboratory

8

The University of Rhode Island

A SUCCESS STORY

On a steep hillside sloping down to Narragansett Bay stands the Graduate School of Oceanography of the University of Rhode Island. Once a small marine-biology station appended to an obscure New England agricultural school (as one old-time faculty member described it), the GSO is now one of the leaders in oceanographic research of the East Coast, if not of the entire United States.

The credit for the transformation is due partly to a distinguished scientist and administrator named John Knauss, who has been dean of the school since 1962, partly to a foresighted president and board of regents of URI, who recognized the need for change, and partly to the state legislators who voted the funds. It surely did not hurt, either, that Rhode Island's junior senator, Claiborne Pell, was so enthusiastic about oceanography that he coauthored a book on the subject, and that the tiny state's senior senator, John Pastore, was on the Senate Appropriations Committee. A third champion of the school was the late Congressman John Fogarty, a veteran member of the House Appropriations Committee.

The GSO began modestly enough as a fishery biology station in 1938. A handful of faculty and students were housed in a small building on the site of an Army post, Fort Kearney, which once guarded the entrance to Narragansett Bay. After World War II the Narragansett Marine Laboratory, as it was then called, expanded to a venerable stone farmhouse, but the pace remained leisurely. The master's degree was the only one granted. Every two years a group of students were admitted. They spent one year doing their course work, the next on their theses. Degrees were awarded, and the next fall a new batch of students was admitted.

However, change slowly crept in. In the early 1950's URI received a large government contract for a study of Narragansett Bay. The study was chiefly physical and geological, adding new dimensions to the capabilities of the Narragansett Marine Laboratory. It also led to two more contracts. One was a classified investigation for the Navy, dealing with the behavior of mines on the sea bottom. The other dealt with the transmission of sound via water and via bottom sediments. Again the institution's strength in fields beyond biology grew, to the point where the university established a master's degree in geological oceanography. And in 1958 the regents of URI decided to grant its first Ph.D. in biological oceanography.

A catastrophe may have been the crucial factor. In 1959 the ancient stone building housing the lab was destroyed by fire. Equipment, specimens, data, records, and years of research literally went up in smoke. The faculty and students had to begin again from scratch. While the present facilities were being constructed, the university found space for them in various departments on the main campus in Kingston, six miles away. Some were quartered in a former county jail.

While things were in this unsettled state, the recently appointed president of URI decided to create a full-scale school of oceanography of such distinction that it would put URI on the map, academically speaking. A student could earn a PhD in chemistry, history, or economics anywhere. But oceanographic schools at that time were still rare. The regents agreed, and in 1961 the GSO was established as an independent graduate division of the university. (Previously the Narragansett Marine Laboratory had been a part of the College of Arts and Sciences.)

To broaden the outlook of the new graduate school, it was decided to bring in a nonbiologist to head it. This was John Knauss, a physical oceanographer who had been at Scripps. With Scripps as a model, Knauss quickly moved to strengthen the GSO in every branch of oceanography. His progress toward this goal was aided by the fact that he brought with him URI's first real oceanographic research vessel, a converted Army freighter. Over the years, URI branched out into new marine activities: marine management; the Law of the Sea; a program for teaching fishery technology and management to commercial fishermen. In 1968 the URI Sea Grant program began, expanding and broadening the marine advisory service that the GSO's Marine Experiment Station was already providing to fishermen.

Today a research complex is blossoming on the Narragansett campus, which the GSO shares with an EPA laboratory for water hygiene and quality, a NOAA game-fish research laboratory, a state nuclear-science center, and labs for ocean engineering. The headquarters of the Division of Marine Resources (an applied-research group) are also on campus.

The GSO still operates on the site of defunct Fort Kearney. Some of its buildings have been erected on the foundations of the old fortifications, and down near the water a number of crumbling gun emplacements still stand, mementos of a pre-air-force, pre-nuclear-bomb era. The building program has not caught up with the expansion of URI's marine programs. A score of trailers house Sea Grant and other personnel, and some of the laboratory and office buildings are in the "temporary" government style. At the time I visited the campus, a collection of disused equipment tucked away in a far corner included cable drums, parts of dredges, pressure tanks, air blowers, a huge, doughnut-shaped float, and an underwater observation chamber. (It was explained to me later that every oceanographic institution has a similar pile of equipment that is not being used at present but is too expensive to throw away.) Down at the bay is a small, pleasant beach where students and faculty eat lunch and swim during the warm weather.

The campus is dominated by the brooding, gray concrete hulk of the nuclear-science building's reactor. Next door is the handsome, modern Claiborne Pell Marine Science Library, which contains over 16,000 volumes and an active file of more than 16,000 reprints of scientific papers. The library receives over 900 scientific journals. It is also the National Sea Grant Depository, the central file for Sea Grant publications from every location in the country. The library is open around the clock for students with a heavy load of research to do.

The GSO is deeply involved in basic research in all fields of oceanography. One current project is a major investigation of the transport of chemicals to the ocean. Recent studies indicate that the chief source of ocean pollution is the air, which carries tiny particles of pesticide residues, PCBs (polychlorinated biphenyls) and other toxic industrial materials, lead compounds, radioactive wastes from nuclear-weapon tests, and the like. (Runoff from the land is mainly local in its effects, although these may be highly visible.) The GSO team is a leader in this field of investigation.

Another major research program concerns the ecology of salt

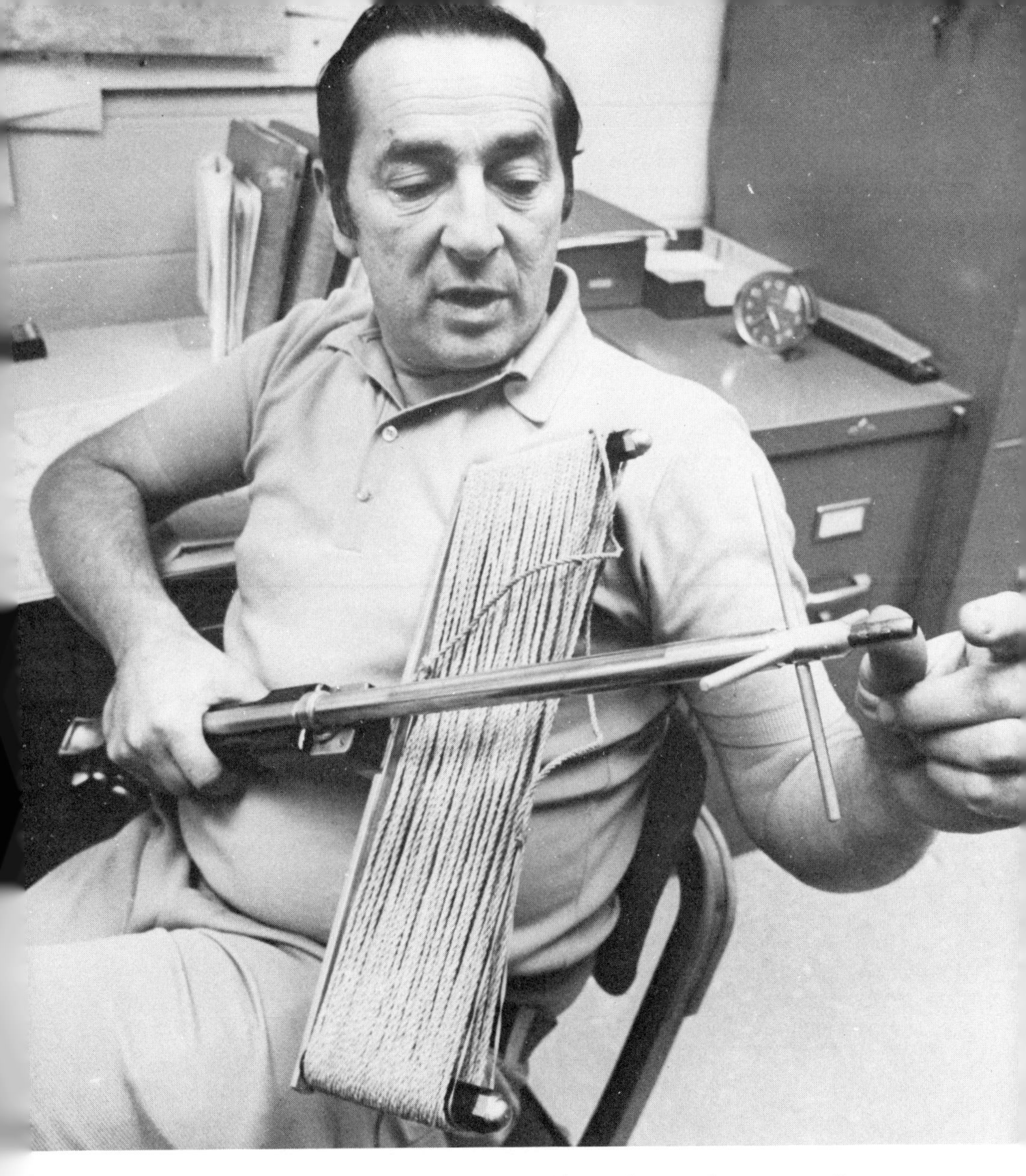

URI biologist Howard E. Winn displays the biopsy dart gun he uses to collect skin samples from free-swimming whales at sea. From the samples, Dr. Winn can tell many things, including even the sex of the whale.
University of Rhode Island

marshes and coastal regions, important for a state like Rhode Island with its long, low-lying shoreline. Biological oceanographers at the GSO have been working with a complex ecological computer model of Narragansett Bay. Developed by a student as his doctoral project and refined periodically since then, the model can predict the outcomes of a variety of alterations in the bay's conditions. For example, if the population of Providence increases so that an additional sewage-treatment plant must be built, the model can predict what effect the added nitrate from the sewage will have on the plankton population of the bay.

GSO scientists usually work on at least three research grants at a time. One scientist has four going, all of them involving seafloor cores from the Antarctic; he is investigating their stratigraphy, fossil content, trace metals, and oxygen isotopes.

A GSO team is contributing to CLIMAP, a study of world climates during the ice ages and an attempt to learn the causes of long-term climatic changes. The data come from deep-sea sediment cores. Fossil plankton organisms give clues to water temperatures at the time each stratum was laid down (radioactive dating confirms the ages of the samples). Thanks to the cooperative efforts of scientists from many institutions, a world-climate map of the last ice age, about 18,000 years ago, has been prepared, and another of a warm interglacial period some 120,000 years ago.

Physical oceanographers from GSO are involved in the MODE (Mid-Ocean Dynamics Experiment) program, a large-scale, intensive study of deep-ocean currents in the Atlantic between Bermuda and the Bahamas, and in POLYMODE, an extension of MODE in which Russian scientists are participating. Others are measuring tropical currents and weather patterns in the Pacific.

The largest project at the GSO is called MERLE (Marine Ecosystems Research Laboratory Experiment). Just getting under way when I visited the GSO in the late summer of 1976, MERLE is an attempt to gain knowledge about the effects of chronic, low-level pollution on a marine ecosystem—specifically, that of Narragansett Bay. There have been other studies of low-level chronic pollution's effects, but they have been limited to one or two species of organisms at a time, not an entire ecosystem. MERLE is examining the effects of pollutants on entire, naturally occurring communities of plankton and small bottom-dwelling organisms. Why test these little "bugs" instead of oysters, flounders, and lobsters? Because the "bugs" are the basis of the food chain, and if they are harmed, it means less food for all the creatures that depend on them, directly or indirectly. This in turn means a drop in the numbers of the fish and shellfish that man eats.

MERLE got an initial funding from the EPA of $2 million for a two-year term. Scientists from five other institutions will conduct experiments at URI while it is in progress. The first experiments were with oil. Later ones were planned to study the effects of trace amounts of heavy metals and of various combinations of pollutants that are ordinarily found in coastal areas. The marine-life communities are kept in nine large tanks, six feet in diameter and eighteen feet deep, lined with fiberglass to avoid chance contamination with metal ions. During any one experiment, three tanks are kept uncontaminated as controls, whereas the others have varying levels of pollutants added.

For each experiment, the tanks are filled with natural water from Narragansett Bay, and the scientists wait until the eggs and spores present in the water hatch out and the tiny plant and animal organisms reach an equilibrium. At the time of my visit, work was still in progress on the wooden pier that holds the tanks, and not all of them had been installed. However, I was able to investigate a few that had already been filled with water, and I noticed that they looked cloudy. My scientist guide explained that I had just seen a miniature plankton bloom, and that it probably happened because a storm a few days ago had stirred up the bay and brought fresh nutrients to the surface layers of the water.

A large lab for analyzing the results of the MERLE program has been completed since then. Some early results are the stabilization of the animal and plant communities in the tanks, thus creat-

Huge fiberglass-lined tanks hold miniature ecosystems for study at the University of Rhode Island's MERLE facility. MERLE stands for Marine Ecosystems Research Laboratory Experiment.

University of Rhode Island

ing miniature Narragansett ecosystems, and the introduction of small amounts of petroleum into the tanks. The initial dose was very low and was not picked up by the organisms or the sediments in the tanks.

MERLE is an East Coast analog to the University of British Columbia's CEPEX (Controlled Ecosystem Pollution Experiment) study in the northern Pacific. However, CEPEX uses gigantic plastic bags moored in the sea, which creates certain problems. MERLE would appear to be a much more easily manageable system. In any case, scientists on the two projects work closely together and share their data.

A few of the GSO's other programs include a study of the sounds made by toadfish and whales, numerous plankton studies—including the effects of red and infrared light on plankton growth—and the effects of volcanic activity on the oceanic crust. Some of the Sea Grant programs are interesting, too. One of them resulted in the development of a breakwater made of junked auto tires. The tires, roped together in bunches, were positioned vertically in the water. Air trapped in the tops of the tires kept them afloat. Bunches of tires were tied together to make a long chain, anchored at each end. The resulting floating breakwater was able

A URI graduate student devised cinder-block "homes" for lobsters as part of his doctoral project.

University of Rhode Island

to reduce three-foot waves to less than one foot. Several small-boat marinas have tried these floating-tire breakwaters and found them very satisfactory. As an unexpected bonus, seaweed and barnacles grow on the tires, providing food for small fish that attract larger fish.

Chemical oceanographers funded by Sea Grant developed methods of identifying components of spilled oil that dissolve in water, thus gaining the ability to "fingerprint" spilled oil more accurately. Researchers found that when they froze an oil sample with liquid nitrogen to a temperature of −187°C. (−330°F.) and shone infrared light through it, they were able to match oil samples from a spill and the suspected source.

URI's Sea Grant program emphasizes fisheries and aquaculture. One program encourages fishermen to catch the deep-dwelling and plentiful red crab and other previously underutilized species. Other programs helped to set up several aquaculture businesses in Rhode Island, among them, salmon raising. Packing plants that handled red crabs found that they had to dispose of masses of waste—shells, guts, and meat that the processing machinery did not extract. At the same time, the salmon raisers complained to the Sea Grant advisers that their fish had pallid, unappealing flesh that made marketing a problem. Sea Grant researchers found that grinding up the crab waste and adding it to the rations fed the salmon restored the appetizing pink flesh color. Two problems were solved, and a troublesome waste became a valuable by-product.

Another Sea Grant study at URI involves the "red tide," a periodic phenomenon caused by a population explosion of certain species of red-colored algae. Unfortunately, red tides are more than a colorful spectacle, for the algae secrete extremely toxic poisons. Millions of fish may be killed by a red-tide infestation. And, although mollusks are not harmed by the poisons, they concentrate them so that humans who eat the mollusks are sometimes killed. The Sea Grant researchers were able to identify several of the red-tide poisons and begin work on developing antidotes.

A major endeavor conducted under the auspices of Sea Grant is the marine-education program. Run from an office in a trailer by an enthusiastic former high-school science teacher named Prentiss Stout, it provides ocean-related curriculum materials for teachers from elementary through high school. During the summer it arranges popular-level marine-education courses for adults.

URI has several other ocean-related programs. One is a program of ocean engineering, which grants undergraduate as well as graduate degrees. Another was the prestigious Law of the Sea Institute, which moved in 1976 to the University of Hawaii. Located on the main URI campus in Kingston, the institute was run by Dr. Knauss, who has served for several years on the United States delegation to the UN conferences on the Law of the Sea. "Law of the Sea" is a broad term that includes such traditional concerns of maritime law as salvage, collision, fisheries, and the extent of national sovereignty over coastal waters. It also covers topics of growing current importance such as pollution, the right to exploit the mineral resources of the seafloor, and the right of coastal nations to bar scientific investigations in their waters. The institute was an international center through which marine scientists and legal experts from countries in all stages of development were able to exchange knowledge and ideas. Its significance lay not only in its work, but also in that it represented a broadening of the concerns of oceanographic institutions.

The Law of the Sea Institute was succeeded at URI by the Center for Ocean Management Studies, designed as a focus for research into the problems of managing American coastal resources. Here administrators can gain a basic knowledge of ocean science, and ocean scientists can get a grounding in the social, legal, political, and economic aspects of marine science. The center runs workshops and meetings in addition to sponsoring short-term research projects.

Dr. Knauss is justifiably proud of the Center for Ocean Management Studies and the Law of the Sea Institute. He is also proud of the amount of attention his students receive from the faculty. GSO students take part in most of the scientific investigations. Often they begin as unskilled technicians; as they acquire skills and expertise, they take a more active role. In many cases they run their own investigations. Advanced students may help to write up proposals for new projects. Other strong points Dr. Knauss mentioned were the diversity of URI's oceanographic and marine-science programs, its close work with the public and the state government in providing advisory services, and its record of basic-science research.

Since most of the funding now available is tied to applied rather than basic research, the focus of URI's investigations may change. However, as Dr. Knauss pointed out, the most important factor in making a good scientific institution is to have good faculty and researchers, and the caliber of URI's scientists will probably not change.

9

Lamont-Doherty

AN OCEANOGRAPHIC INSTITUTION IN DISGUISE

One of the leading oceanographic institutions in the United States, if not in the world, doesn't even have the word "oceanographic" in its name. Yet the Lamont–Doherty Geological Observatory is one of the Big Three in oceanographic research, and in geological and geophysical oceanography it is number one.

Lamont-Doherty, to give it its usual name, is part of Columbia University's geology department. It lies about a half hour's drive from Columbia, across the Hudson River in Rockland County, right on the New York–New Jersey state line. Like most oceanographic institutions, it is open only to graduate students. Today it has a staff of about 500, including about 120 scientists of various ranks and 80 to 90 students.

Lamont-Doherty* was founded in 1948 by Maurice Ewing, then a professor of geology at Columbia. Thomas Lamont, a wealthy banker, had died, and his wife offered the 125-acre estate to Columbia, along with half a million dollars for operating expenses. Torrey Cliff, as the estate was then called, was offered first to the Columbia Medical School, but the medics turned it

* The name was originally Lamont. It was changed in 1969 after a philanthropic couple, Henry and Grace Doherty, left the institution a large endowment.

down. Thus it fell to Ewing, who for some time had been agitating for a seismographic laboratory site far from the earth-shaking subways and street traffic of New York's upper West Side.

The estate to which Ewing fell heir is located dramatically on a cliff overlooking the Hudson, although the spectacular view is now blocked by trees planted to screen the lab buildings from neighbors. (Rockland County once sheltered a number of artists' colonies, and the resident creative people did not welcome the idea of a big laboratory being built in their backyards.) At the time of the offer, however, Ewing's chief concern was that the rock of the Palisades, on which the house was built, was too fractured to transmit seismic waves properly. A hurried trip out with a seismograph convinced him that the site was acceptable.

The next problem was where to find working space. The original gift included only the mansion, a greenhouse, an enclosed swimming pool, a huge garage, and various gardeners' cottages. At first, the mansion was turned, room by room, into labs and offices. The seismograph was set up in the former root cellar. The garage became a core "library"; the greenhouse was transformed into a machine shop where Ewing and his colleagues tinkered with worn-out instruments and converted them into entirely new devices.

This parsimony was necessary because the new geological observatory was self-supporting. And it took time before the necessary grants and contracts came trickling in. In the early days, Lamont operated on such a tight budget that Ewing and his students would spend a week building a galvanometer rather than lay out thirty dollars to buy one. The spirit of frugality still endures.

The first year there were about two dozen scientists and students at Lamont, and more were added each year until Ewing had to keep some of them out at sea in order to make room for the rest. Eventually, enough money came in to construct proper lab facilities, and the handsome old mansion behind its rose garden and apple trees now houses only the library. The old indoor swimming pool, covered over, has become the cafeteria. In all, there are now eighteen buildings, all within easy walking distance of each other.

Most of the top-ranking marine-science schools reflect the personality of a dynamic director. Lamont, more than most, bears the stamp of the hard-driving, multi-talented Ewing.

W. Maurice Ewing* was born in Texas in 1906; he died in 1974, shortly before his sixty-eighth birthday. A large, physically pow-

---

* The W. stands for William, which Ewing never used and legally dropped in later life.

erful man, in his later years he sported a shock of white hair that made him look mellow and professorial. The appearance was deceiving, for according to all accounts Ewing was anything but mellow. A thorough perfectionist, he was impatient with work that didn't measure up to his own standards.

Although Ewing may have contributed more to oceanographic knowledge than any other individual in this century, he did not regard himself as an oceanographer at all. He insisted that he was a geologist and that the ocean was nothing but "a murky mist that keeps me from seeing the bottom." He was also a superlative teacher, and many of his students, such as Bruce Heezen, Frank Press of MIT, J. Lamar Worzel of the University of Texas, and Lamont-Doherty's present director, Manik Talwani, went on to become prominent geological oceanographers themselves.

At first, Lamont's researchers had no research vessel of their own. They had to wangle space aboard other institutions' ships. As a result, they spent about three months of each year collecting data and the other nine months working on them. But in 1953

The converted yacht *Vema,* workhorse of Lamont-Doherty's oceanographic research fleet, returns from a cruise.
Lamont-Doherty Geological Observatory

Launching a pop-up current meter from R/V Conrad in the chilly Indian Ocean between South Africa and Antarctica. The two barrel-shaped floats will return the meter to the surface after a month of recording data at the ocean bottom.
Lamont-Doherty Geological Observatory

Lamont acquired the *Vema,* a former racing yacht, whose unusual name is an acronym of *Ma*ud *Ve*tlesen, a former owner's wife. *Vema* came equipped with three masts and for several years carried sails to steady her on her oceanographic voyages. Once, when the engines failed, *Vema* sailed home from the Gulf of Mexico. Sails and masts are gone now, and the ship's proud figurehead, a white-and-gold eagle, stands outside the Oceanographic Building of Lamont. But *Vema*'s sturdy hull of Swedish wrought iron is still at sea for some 300 days every year, though the vessel is now more than fifty years old. Eventually *Vema* was supplemented by the *Robert Conrad,* doubling Lamont's capacity for sea time.

One of Lamont's early triumphs was the discovery of great turbidity currents in the ocean, which the scientists proved were responsible for carving canyons in the continental shelves and filling the deep ocean basins with sediments to form the abyssal plains.

A turbidity current is a current caused by a flow of fine sediments—sand, mud, or clay—suspended in the water. The weight of the tiny sediment particles gives momentum to the water mass that carries them. When a turbidity current starts, the cloud of murky water flows down a seafloor slope like an underwater avalanche, gathering speed and force as it goes, until it reaches a level area and gradually runs out of energy. The power

Professor Maurice Ewing, pointer in hand, examines split core samples at Lamont-Doherty. Desiccation has caused the core samples to crack and warp, but does not alter their basic constituents.

Lamont-Doherty Geological Observatory

of a turbidity current is almost unimaginable. It not only rips deep furrows in soft sediments; it even wears away solid rock.

By the 1940's the existence of turbidity currents had long been known, but geologists thought they were limited to mountain lakes. Anyone who suggested that they might have something to do with shaping the submarine landscape was pooh-poohed.

In May 1949 Ewing was unexpectedly offered four days of ship time on a Woods Hole vessel that was returning from a cruise to southern waters. He could not bring himself to turn down the offer, even though it meant he had to fly his scientific team and a ton of lead for coring weights to Florida within forty-eight hours.

Half a day out, a tremendous storm forced the vessel to heave to and ride it out. The Gulf Stream carried the ship hundreds of miles to the north, much too far to return to the Blake Plateau, where Ewing had wanted to take cores. The captain of the vessel suggested meaningfully that they might as well run back to Woods Hole, since they had so little time left anyway.

But Ewing, always prepared to extract some good from even the worst of situations, insisted that the ship stay out. Since they were not far from the latitude of New York, he decided to trace the course of the Hudson Canyon. The ship followed the canyon for 105 miles *beyond* the edge of the continental shelf, where oceanographers had thought it ended, before it had to turn back for lack of time. At this point the canyon, under 11,000 feet of water, was still 900 feet deep, and the end was nowhere in sight (it was later traced nearly one hundred miles farther before it petered out in an abyssal plain). Curiously, cores from this deep-lying bottom showed shallow-water shells. How had they gotten there? A few other cruises that summer and fall turned up more unexplained evidence that seemed to fit only one theory: the derided idea of a turbidity current.

After investigating the Hudson Canyon, Ewing and his group wanted to get some idea of the size and force of a turbidity current. Clues pointed to the Grand Banks earthquake of 1929 as a prime candidate for investigation. The epicenter of that severe earthquake, which was felt as far away as New York City, was on the continental slope south of Newfoundland. That area was a main street for transatlantic cables, and over a dozen of the cables were broken. Curiously enough, they did not break at the same time, but one after another, with the last one breaking twelve hours after the first one. The cables on the continental shelf, inshore from the slope, did not break at all. It seemed obvious to the Lamont crew that a turbidity current was the cause.

Seismic profiling revealed that a chunk of sediment 150 miles long, 80 miles wide, and 1,200 feet thick had been knocked loose

A curator removes a tiny portion of a core sample for study at the new Lamont-Doherty core lab.

Lamont-Doherty Geological Observatory

from the continental slope and tobogganed downhill, creating a huge and violent turbidity current. Ewing and Heezen calculated that at one point the current reached a velocity of more than 50 miles an hour, an unheard-of speed for flowing water. Another scientist estimated the flow of the current at 600 times that of the lower Mississippi River. It took three summers to get cores from the area—the weather was too dangerous the first two years. But eventually a graduate student got a series of cores along a line where a *200-mile-long* section of cable had been carried away. The cores showed the typical graded sediments of a turbidity current—fine particles on top, coarse ones on bottom—overlying the normal clay of the deep plain, with a sharp boundary line in between.

During the next few years Lamont investigated more turbidity currents. As the evidence mounted, the skeptics one after another yielded. By 1960 turbidity currents were almost universally accepted as a major force in the shaping of the seafloor. The study of turbidity currents had some interesting ramifications. For one thing, close study of the fossils in the cores led to a revision of the geologic time scale, making the Pleistocene and its ice ages start much earlier than had been previously believed. For another,

The late Dr. Bruce Heezen points to the Mid-Atlantic Rift (his joint discovery) on a relief model of the globe. Dr. Heezen died at sea in the summer of 1977 while preparing for a dive in the research submersible *Alvin*.

Lamont-Doherty Geological Observatory

Lamont scientists found evidence that turbidity currents are connected with the formation of petroleum. The theory is that turbidity currents bury great masses of tiny plankton creatures so that they decay in the absence of oxygen. Under these conditions their fats and oils turn to petroleum. In 1974 two Lamont investigators actually extracted petroleum from turbidity-current sediment cores, strong evidence for the theory.

We have already mentioned Lamont's great contribution to the story of the discovery of the midocean rift. In 1952 Bruce Heezen and his assistant, Marie Tharp, were plotting profiles of sections taken across the Mid-Atlantic Ridge. As Tharp, the cartographer, worked her way from north to south, she noticed what seemed to be a deep notch in the middle of the ridge in several profiles. Turning to Heezen, she said, "Say, Bruce, doesn't this look like a rift valley in here?"

Heezen pooh-poohed this idea as "girl talk" and for a year paid no attention to it. Then he got a contract to study cable routes, which involved locating zones of potential danger such as earthquakes. He had another draftsman plot the epicenters of recent midocean quakes on Marie Tharp's map. They fell along a narrow band, right in what she had said was a rift valley. Once more, chance had led to an important scientific discovery. Subsequent studies showed that the rift was indeed a rift, which fitted the last piece into the puzzle of plate tectonics. Studies of heat flow and magnetism provided the final proof.

Arctic research is another Lamont–Doherty specialty. The Arctic Ocean is a unique case because it is always ice-covered. As a result, it cannot be studied from a conventional oceanographic research vessel. Some oceanographic institutions send researchers out with Coast Guard icebreakers for limited tours. Lamont flies its research teams up to Point Barrow, Alaska, or other convenient base points on the Arctic shore, and ferries them out to a drifting ice floe by small planes. A fully equipped field lab is set up on the ice, and for six weeks the scientists measure current velocities, winds, water temperature and salinity, and similar data that have a bearing on the Arctic climate. Other objectives of the

A lead (channel) begins to open in the ice beneath the main camp of AIDJEX. The widening fissure eventually forced abandonment of the camp.
Lamont-Doherty Geological Observatory

Two AIDJEX participants track a bright orange weather balloon to map direction and velocity of air currents.

Lamont-Doherty Geological Observatory

Arctic program are to learn how large masses of sea ice behave under stress and to find out more about the role of eddies in transporting energy in the oceans. A more ambitious project was planned for 1978, using a Coast Guard icebreaker frozen into the pack ice as a drifting lab for geophysical measurements.

The Arctic investigation program also has links to the search for the causes of the ice ages. Ewing and his colleague William L. Donn once proposed a controversial theory that the ice ages were triggered by the thawing of the Arctic Ocean. Once the surface of the Arctic was free of ice, they suggested, so much water evaporated that the Northern Hemisphere received excessively heavy snowfalls. So much snow fell that it did not melt entirely away in the summers; bit by bit it built up into the massive ice sheets that spread under their own weight until they covered a large part of the globe. At the same time, the snow and ice reflected a good deal of the sun's radiation, cooling the Earth further and making more snow and ice accumulate. The cycle did not come to a halt until the Arctic Ocean once more froze over, cutting off the supply of moisture.

The Ewing–Donn theory has now been exploded, however, and by a fellow Lamont scientist, James D. Hays. A team of American and British scientists led by Hays had been examining cores from the Indian Ocean as one of the programs of Project CLIMAP. (CLIMAP stands for Climate Long-Range Investigation, Mapping, and Prediction, and it is a joint program involving a number of universities.) The cores Hays's group was studying provided fossils dating back as far as 450,000 years ago. The fossils, of tiny protozoans called radiolaria, gave evidence of the temperature of the ocean at the time when they died and drifted down to the sea floor. Certain species of radiolaria thrive in warm water, others in cold. Thus, a layer of cold-loving radiolaria shells must have been laid down in a cold period, warmth-loving radiolaria in a warm period. For confirmation, the scientists checked the ratios of normal oxygen and the heavy isotope 0-18 in the fossils. In cold periods, seawater contains a higher proportion of 0-18 than in warm periods, because normal oxygen (0-16) has a slightly greater tendency to get locked up in ice. The results checked perfectly.

Warm-water fossils and cold-water fossils alternated in a regular pattern of about 93,000 years. The Hays team found another pattern with a cycle of about 42,000 years. They cranked their data into the computer and found that the 93,000-year cycles

Muffled against the Arctic cold, Lamont-Doherty scientists explore pressure ridges in the pack ice. Scientist at right carries a rifle for protection against bears and to signal for help if lost.

Kenneth J. Hunkins, Lamont-Doherty Geological Observatory

Plate 6
2a
2b
2c
1
2d

corresponded closely with the variations in the Earth's orbit from elliptical to circular. The shorter cycles matched the variations in the inclination of Earth's axis toward the sun. These changes altered the amount and the seasonal distribution of solar radiation received by the Earth, warming or cooling the entire planet and either melting each winter's snow away or allowing it to accumulate for millennia. With this knowledge, says Hays, it should be possible to predict the onset of the next ice age.

Another Lamont scientist involved in CLIMAP is Dr. Allan Bé, a specialist in foraminifera. These one-celled organisms—called forams for short—build intricate shells of calcium carbonate. Many species are planktonic. Others live on the seafloor or attached to other organisms. Dr. Bé and his colleagues collect forams from warm and cold waters, and from various depths. They raise certain species under controlled conditions in the lab. (This work is done at the Bermuda Biological Station.) They study the forams' growth rates, life spans, reproductive rates, responses to changes in their environment, nutritional needs, and other aspects of their life cycles. Their findings, applied to fossil foram shells, give additional evidence about the climates of prehistoric periods.

We have mentioned here Lamont-Doherty's outstanding contributions to scientific knowedge. There are many other programs that we have no room to list, but all of them contribute in some way.

Photomicrographs, enlarged two hundred times, show the intricate structure of a foraminiferan as seen from different angles. Skeletons of these microscopic carnivores are invaluable evidence in the study of ancient climates.

Dr. Alan Bé, Lamont-Doherty Geological Observatory

10

Stony Brook

A UNIT IN A BIG STATE SYSTEM

Some fifty-eight miles east of the New York City line lies the Stony Brook campus of the sprawling State University of New York. Three modernistic buildings at Stony Brook house the Marine Sciences Research Center, established in the 1960's as *the* oceanographic research department for the entire SUNY system. It is also the only unit of SUNY that offers graduate degrees in oceanography and marine-environmental studies.

The MSRC was originally established as a research institution. It did not have a degree program until 1970. Since then, it has evolved increasingly toward the training of oceanographers, although it is still oriented more toward research than toward teaching. Public service is its third goal, in addition to research and education. Some thirty scientists and forty students work to fulfill these objectives.

Although the MSRC's scientists take part in plenty of deep-water projects, the center's major emphasis is on coastal and estuarine research, particularly on assessing man's impact on coastal waters. The companion effort is developing management strategies to conserve and to rehabilitate, when necessary, the coastal marine environment. In fact, the center's promotional literature, making a virtue out of necessity, points out that the

Students prepare to take water samples with a Nansen bottle near Throgs Neck Bridge.

Marine Sciences Research Center, State University of New York

proximity of New York City and the growing populations of Long Island and Connecticut make the coastal waters of New York an excellent laboratory for studying methods of pollution abatement and coastal-zone management.

The center's 55-foot research vessel *Onrust* is fitted out with grab samplers, trawls, plankton nets, corers, computer, wet lab, and all kinds of electronic navigation and depth-recording equipment. It also has a submersible pump for obtaining water samples from any specified depth up to twenty feet, far more effectively than a Nansen bottle. (A Nansen bottle is a bottle-shaped container that is lowered into the water on a wire cable. At the desired depth, it closes automatically.) The center also has a number of smaller vessels for near-shore work in protected waters.

The scientists of the Marine Sciences Research Center strive to keep a balance between basic and applied research. There are active investigation projects in biological, chemical, geological, and physical oceanography, as well as in fishery and coastal-zone management. Rather than leave the results of their research entombed in professional journals, where only their peers would read them, the center's scientists are committed to translating their own findings and those of others into forms that are usable by decision makers when societal problems need resolving. It is this feature, the director told me, that perhaps distinguishes the MSRC from other oceanographic institutions.

One of the major research programs is conducted by Dr. Charles F. Wurster and colleagues at Flax Pond, a quarter square mile of salt marsh not far from the campus. Surrounded by large estates, Flax Pond remains relatively unpolluted by sewage and runoff from streets and lawns, making it a good experimental location.

Dr. Wurster, a long-time, dedicated environmentalist, has specialized in studying the effects of chlorinated hydrocarbons, such as DDT, other pesticides, and PCBs (polychlorinated biphenyls), on various forms of life, especially phytoplankton. He also wrote much of the original litigation that led to the ban on the use of DDT.

In talking with Dr. Wurster, I learned some new things about the behavior of DDT in the biosphere. It is generally believed that living organisms cannot get rid of DDT, but simply store it up in their tissues until it reaches lethal proportions. Actually, the body does eventually get rid of its DDT content, though much too slowly to do any good when it keeps getting new doses of the wonder pesticide from the environment. It is also generally believed that DDT does not break down, but keeps its toxicity for an indefinite number of years. Chemists have learned that it does break down—again, very, very slowly. Unfortunately, one of its breakdown products is a very similar chemical known as DDE, which is somewhat less toxic but is even more long-lived.

At Flax Pond, Dr. Wurster and several associates grow cultures of native plankton organisms from the pond in sealed plastic bags about the size of a bologna sausage. The bags are suspended in the pond in protective mesh tubes strung from a raft. The water in the bags, taken from the pond, is dosed with measured quantities of the various hydrocarbon pollutants. Careful daily records are taken of such parameters as species present, size distribution, optical counts, photosynthesis, and growth rates of the treated plankton compared with those of control samples in bags with clean water. The scientists also measure how much of each pollutant the plankton organisms accumulate. This is vital in determining how rapidly a pollutant spreads through the food web. Since the plastic material of the bags is semipermeable, the plankton and large molecules, such as the hydrocarbons, stay trapped inside, whereas water and dissolved nutrients pass freely in and out.

The Flax Pond program grew out of a series of laboratory experiments that involved cultures of several species of marine phytoplankton organisms. These experiments were criticized by some as being insufficiently related to natural conditions; at Flax Pond everything is natural—light, water chemistry, temperature, and plant associations—except for the plastic bags, which provide the necessary degree of control.

Unlike the CEPEX and MERLE experiments, the Flax Pond experiment is small in scale, in time as well as in size. Whereas the time scale of the first two is measured in years, Flax Pond's is measured in days to a week or two. Work goes on all year except in the winter, when the sunlight is too feeble for photosynthesis and the low temperatures slow down the metabolism of all the organisms that are not dead or dormant. Winter also interferes with the experimenters' ability to do their work. The act of taking samples involves delicate manipulations, which cannot be performed with gloves on. But without gloves, the experimenters' fingers quickly become too stiff with cold to do the work anyway. Man has not yet figured out how to circumvent every aspect of nature.

In an entirely different field is the work of Dr. Peter Weyl, an eminent physical oceanographer and specialist in coastal-zone planning. Dr. Weyl has been involved with CLIMAP, a project under the International Decade of Ocean Exploration for studying the long-term variations in the Earth's climate and the part the oceans have played in these variations. Dr. Weyl is attempting to utilize the results obtained by other investigators to reconstruct the behavior of the oceans during the height of the last ice age, some 18,000 years ago. At that time the Gulf Stream flowed due east from North America and then turned south off Portugal, so that its warming influence did not reach northwestern Europe.

Fisheries management is the specialty of Dr. J. L. McHugh, who began his marine career in 1927 as a high-school student with a summer job on a fishing boat in his native British Columbia. Dr.

McHugh's path led him to Scripps and later to a series of positions with various fishery agencies, and, eventually, to Stony Brook. He has also served as the United States commissioner on the International Whaling Commission and the Inter-American Tropical Tuna Commission, among others.

Dr. McHugh spoke at some length about his work on the International Whaling Commission, on which he served from 1961 to 1972, and about the world whale situation. He feels that the IWC, much criticized for ineffectuality, has actually been doing an increasingly effective job since 1965, and that its critics are basing their complaints on out-of-date information.

Dr. McHugh disagrees strongly with those people (including the author) who feel that it is morally wrong to kill whales and dolphins because they are intelligent fellow mammals. He holds the view that whales are as much a marine resource as tuna or oysters, and that man has a right to exploit them for his own use. But, as a good conservationist, he is horrified by the mass slaughter that has brought many whale species close to the vanishing point, and he is as anxious as anyone to restore the vanished whale herds. Where he differs from the whale preservationists is on method. He feels that to adopt the ten-year moratorium on whale killing that many environmentalists have urged would be counterproductive, since it might well lead to the two remaining major whaling nations—Russia and Japan—dropping out of the IWC and taking whales without any regulation at all. Instead, he favors permitting them to go on taking a limited number of whales from nonendangered species, while forbidding the taking of endangered species until their numbers have come back to safe levels.

Whales reproduce so slowly, he told me, that even as low a catch as 5 percent of the population of any one species will keep that species from increasing. Any larger catch means a downward spiral. To permit the herds to recover requires complete protection or else limiting the catch to 1 or 2 percent of the population, depending on how badly depleted the species is. Unfortunately, science still does not have sufficient data to make a realistic estimate of whale populations, and a side benefit of limited whaling would be the accumulation of the information needed for this.

In fishing, as in whaling, some sort of regulation is badly needed to preserve the fish stocks at an exploitable level. But, Dr. McHugh pointed out, if there are twenty nations engaged in fishing for cod in the North Atlantic, and one of them decides to limit its catch in the interests of conservation, it will do no good. The only result will be that the other nineteen nations will catch what that one nation altruistically left. For conservation measures to work, everyone must follow them. And, since man is not altruistic by nature, a strong international policing agency is probably necessary to manage the fisheries of the open sea for maximum sustained yield.

The same sort of policing will be necessary to salvage our domestic inshore fisheries. Here the conflict is not between fishermen of different nations, but between those of different states and between those who fish for a living and those who fish for sport. For years sport and commercial fishermen have accused each other of depleting the fish population by reckless overfishing. And here Dr. McHugh mentioned an interesting paradox.

Take, for example, a sport fisherman who goes out to the shore for a day to try for striped bass. He stands on the beach, casting his lure into the surf time after time; with luck, his day's efforts may yield him ten fish, pulled in one at a time. At the same time, perhaps under the outraged eyes of that sport fisherman, a commercial fishing boat may net three or four *tons* of fish in a single haul. It would appear that the commercial fisherman poses a much greater threat to the fish. However, as Dr. McHugh pointed out, the number of sport fishermen is so much greater than that of commercial fishermen that their total catch is much larger than the commercial catch.

Again, some balance between the rights of each group must be found, and the regulations must be enforced to keep anyone from taking more than his fair share. Dr. McHugh will have many such problems to adjudicate in his latest off-campus position on the Mid-Atlantic Regional Fishery Management Council.

We spoke also of the contributions of oceanography to fisheries management. They have been many. One example is in discovering the reasons (aside from the size of the previous year's catch) for the up-and-down fluctuations in fish stocks. These may include changes in water temperature and salinity, which cause the fish to migrate to new locations where conditions suit them better; a good or bad plankton crop, on which young fish larvae feed; and fluctuations in the numbers of predators and competing species.

Another example is in predicting the annual migrations of food fishes. In the Pacific, by monitoring changes in temperature and salinity, oceanographers have been able to predict the movements of tuna schools six months in advance. By extrapolating their data, they are also able to make a pretty close prediction of the size of the catch.

Geological oceanography is represented at Stony Brook by the director, Dr. J. R. Schubel, a relatively young man brimming over with ideas. Dr. Schubel's specialty is sediments in all their ramifications: how they form and where they are desposited; how they are transported in the water; how they interact with sea-dwelling organisms. He is also actively involved in coastal management.

Together with Peter Weyl, he has worked on NOAA's gigantic Project MESA (described at length in Chapter 17), which involves dumping various kinds of wastes in New York Bight, and is also furnishing expert advice on dredging and the disposal of dredging spoil in Long Island Sound. A certain amount of dredging is

A student at Stony Brook's Marine Sciences Research Center uses a Secchi disk to measure the turbidity of water in Long Island Sound near the Throgs Neck Bridge.

Marine Sciences Research Center, State University of New York

necessary to keep harbors and shipping channels open. But realistic coastal management calls for disposing of the dredged material where it will do the least harm to environment and ecology. Care must be given to choosing dumping sites where currents will not carry off the spoil and deposit it somewhere else, blanketing the bottom and suffocating life there. Similarly, spoil should not be dumped on a productive fishing ground or oyster bed, or near a bathing beach.

Another kind of dredging is also common along the East Coast—vast quantities of sand and gravel are mined from offshore beds for the construction industry. In fact, New York Harbor is the largest open-pit sand mine in the country.

The process of dredging itself stirs up clouds of sand and mud, which currents carry off. Will this suspended matter interfere with the biological productivity of the water? Where will it eventually settle? These, too, are questions that must be considered before a dredging permit is granted. On the other hand, in some spots dredging may benefit marine life by improving the circulation of the water.

MSRC scientists play important roles in helping the state and the nation resolve environmental crises when they occur. They play an even more important role in anticipating potential crises and in devising strategies to prevent their occurrence. However, MSRC never takes a stand for or against a proposal. The scientists' job is to serve as expert witnesses, giving their opinion, based on research, of the probable consequences of such human activities as dredging, building a marina, filling in wetlands, or building a bridge across Long Island Sound.

By not taking an adversary position and by restricting their testimony to their scientific findings, they keep their testimony objective; thus they can play a far more effective role in the long run in helping work out serious environmental problems. As Dr. Schubel points out, there is rarely a shortage of value judgments on environmental issues, whereas there has characteristically been a shortage of scientific data.

11

The University of Delaware's College of Marine Studies

A SMALL BUT LIVELY INSTITUTION

In northern Delaware, a few miles off the crowded thoroughfare of Interstate 95, is the tidy little town of Newark, the home of the University of Delaware. Its College of Marine Studies was not established until 1970, but it has already made its influence felt in the world of marine science and, to some extent, in the larger world beyond.

The University of Delaware's involvement with marine science actually dates back to 1950, when a marine-biology program was set up at the town of Lewes, on the little state's Atlantic coast. Delaware is not a major maritime state, but with nearly half its borders consisting of the Atlantic Ocean and Delaware Bay, it has a very real interest in the ocean and its behavior. At that time, too, shellfish harvesting and fishing were important in the state's economy. And Delaware's central location makes it a key state in problems involving the Delaware River, Delaware Bay, and the nearby portion of the Atlantic.

The marine biology program grew as it proved its value to the state's citizens. In 1960 the university took another figurative step into the ocean when it chose a marine geologist to head up its geology department. And in 1967 Dean William S. Gaither of the engineering school added a program of ocean engineering, with emphasis on port and coastal engineering.

With the university deeply engaged in marine-science work, the next step was to organize a marine-research division. After much planning and discussion, the College of Marine Studies was set up as one of the university's graduate schools, with Gaither as its dean. Bill Gaither is one of the breed of youthful, dynamic, and highly intelligent men who have been chosen to get the newer, smaller marine-science schools under way. Trained as an engineer, Dean Gaither takes a broad, pragmatic view of his school and its mission. When I asked him whether the CMS did more basic or applied research, he explained that he and his colleagues didn't think in those terms. Their aim was to study the whole spectrum of man's interactions with the sea and to gain a better understanding of the intelligent use of the sea as a resource. Often, in working toward some specified, practical goal, they found they had to do a lot of basic research first.

The University of Delaware is an unusual school in that it is privately run but partly state-supported. Although it ranks among the top twenty universities in the United States in the size of its endowments, it still depends on state money for some 30 percent of its budget. The College of Marine Studies is unusual, too, in that instead of battling to establish its autonomy from the university, it tries to melt in with the other departments. As a result, about half its faculty hold joint appointments, and the CMS is able to share facilities with the other departments instead of spending money on building its own new ones.

In addition to the standard disciplines of biology, physics, chemistry, and geology of the oceans, the CMS features programs in ocean engineering and marine affairs. Much of the teaching and lab work takes place on the main campus in Newark, a pleasant, spacious enclave of ivy-covered Georgian-style brick buildings and big old shade trees. Fieldwork is carried on at the new Marine Studies Center lab complex in Lewes.

The College of Marine Studies is definitely not a blue-water institution. It was established with the particular goal of studying the continental shelf, including its coastal and estuarine waters. The biological program is strongly tilted toward mariculture and fishery studies. All the disciplines are combined to focus on problems of ecological balance and pollution.

The Office of Naval Research has sponsored a number of interesting investigations at Delaware. One, for which the sandy coast of Delaware seems tailor-made, is the movement of sand and the evolution of coastal land forms such as spits, sandbars, dunes, and lagoons. As a part of this study, the researchers had to work out a mathematical model for the formation and behavior of waves as they approach the shore, since waves are major agents in shaping and reshaping a sandy coast. Another ONR project involves the role that major river systems play in the chemical balance of the oceans by adding fresh water, organic matter, and dissolved minerals.

Like every other marine institution, the CMS does a good deal of work on air-sea interactions and surface wave studies. Another aspect of its physical-oceanography work which ONR is pushing is the study of fronts in the water, that is, the boundaries between different water masses. The Navy is interested in learning more about the way these boundary layers affect sound waves.

Other funds for research come from the National Science Foundation, from Sea Grant, from NASA, and from foundations and other private sources.

The ocean engineering program has a solid foundation in such traditional subjects as harbor design, protection of coastlands from erosion, pollution control, and designing artificial islands for industry sites. It is also venturing into the relatively new fields of remote sensing and instrument technology.

The remote-sensing group uses satellites and high-flying aircraft to gather data for such tasks as mapping wetlands and tracing the flow patterns of currents and the paths taken by oil spills. Cameras, infrared sensors, and microwave sensors are the tools they use. The data gathered by the remote sensors, whose height above the earth gives them tremendous scope, are verified by on-the-spot checks made by ships and sensors on the surface. This takes a bit of managing, since both sets of observations must be made at precisely the same time and location.

Some of the technology borders on the exotic. For example, Delaware's researchers are now working on a method of identifying pollutants by the particular wavelengths of light each one reflects. Picked up by remote sensor, these "spectral signatures" can be used to map the concentration of each pollutant.

One of the most important aspects of the CMS is its marine-affairs program, which pulls together a whole spectrum of marine and social sciences. As Dean Gaither pointed out, marine scientists have often been frustrated because of the communication gap between them and the men and women who make and carry out ocean-related policy. The policy-making legislators and administrators, in turn, have often been handicapped by their lack of knowledge in the field they are supposed to be regulating (as Dr. J. L. McHugh of Stony Brook likes to say, laws are usually based on opinions rather than on facts). The marine-affairs program aims to turn out scientists who will be able to translate their knowledge into effective policy and policy-makers who will be familiar with marine-scientific concepts and will also know whom to contact for expert advice. Dean Gaither considers this one of the most fruitful of his institution's efforts, as he feels it is vital to spread knowledge of the ocean's importance to human survival.

A sampling of the problems considered by marine-affairs students, many of whom are professionals in mid-career, would include world energy policy, marine-transportation and government policy, offshore fishery management techniques, and the probable effect on ship traffic through important straits as more coastal nations choose to assert their 200-mile-zone sovereignty. Another would be the legal constraints on aquaculture, chiefly state fish and game laws designed to protect wild resources. Such laws forbid such necessary aquacultural practices as taking shellfish of less than a certain size. They also typically limit the number of hours per day during which the shellfish may be harvested and establish closed seasons when none may be harvested at all. If aquaculture is to become a successful industry, these laws, necessary for conservation, must be adapted to the new situation.

One of Delaware's biggest research programs is the oyster-culture project, which takes the unique approach of raising these succulent bivalves (and clams and mussels too) in a completely controlled environment. Sea Grant, the university, the state, and private industry share the costs of the program, which is carried out at a former oyster-depuration plant at Lewes, a mile or so down the shore from the lab complex. ("Depuration" is a fancy term for getting rid of disease organisms and toxic substances in shellfish to make them safe for humans to eat.)

The oyster-culture program began as an attempt to revitalize the defunct oyster industry of Delaware Bay, which was formerly one of the nation's chief oyster-producing areas. In the 1950's, however, increasing water pollution began to take its toll. Silt, washing down from building sites around the bay, buried many oyster beds and suffocated their inhabitants. Oyster drills (a kind of marine snail), starfish, and other predators further reduced the numbers of oysters. The final blow was the appearance of the deadly disease organism known as MSX, which effectually wiped out the remaining oysters.

At first the CMS researchers concentrated on breeding a disease-resistant oyster. But it became apparent that this was not the answer. What with disease, pesticides, petroleum, predators, and silt, the infant oysters faced too many hazards on their way to maturity. Taking a clue from agriculture, the Delaware aquacul-

In the "oyster greenhouse" at Lewes, Delaware, CMS scientists and engineers raise oysters under optimum growth conditions.
Sea Grant College Program, University of Delaware

turists examined the commercial chicken industry. Chicken growers raise their birds in batches of thousands under completely artificial conditions; not only this—they also grow the chickens to market size in a fraction of the time it takes by the old-fashioned barnyard method. Could such a technique be applied to raising bivalves?

The conclusion was yes, and the Delaware scientists devised a closed-cycle system of oyster culture under which the oyster grower has complete control of every factor of the environment. Since the oysters are raised in tanks on land, they are protected from predators. The water system is self-contained and recirculating; the same water is used over and over. No contaminants get into it. An ultraviolet sterilization system kills disease organisms, and the wastes given off by the oysters can be used to grow the algae on which the oysters feed. The temperature and mineral content of the water can be kept at the best levels to make the oysters grow rapidly.

Every angle of the problem was considered. The diet of oysters in the wild was analyzed, and the four most abundant species of one-celled algae found in the oysters' intestines were isolated. Then cultures of each alga were raised, and the oysters were tested on various mixtures. It was found that they grew fastest on a diet of two species, *Thalassiosira pseudonana* and *Isochrysis galbana*. The researchers also worked with scientists of a big food company to create a series of artificial rations for the oysters, but found that they did better on natural food.

More research went into raising a plentiful and steady crop of algae—the best level of light, of salinity, of temperature, and of nutrients in the water. By adjusting these conditions, the researchers were able to grow algae four times faster than the natural rate of growth.

Meanwhile, other scientists were working on the oyster portion of the problem. They worked out a method of having seed stock (baby oysters) on hand at any time by making the parent oysters spawn on command. This they did by moving the oysters from the holding tanks to a spawning tank with water at a constant temperature of 28 degrees Celsius (82.4 degrees Fahrenheit). The warm water is the biological cue to the oyster to produce eggs and sperm and release them into the water.

The fertilized eggs develop rapidly into microscopic, free-swimming larvae. The larvae are moved to growing tanks where in ten to fourteen days they attach themselves to the nearest hard substance—in this case, thin plastic sheets hung in the water. The newly set spat, as young oysters are called, grow very rapidly under the controlled conditions of their scientifically planned universe. At the time of my visit, they were reaching market size in thirty-six weeks, four times faster than naturally grown oysters. Dean Gaither told me that the scientists at Lewes hoped to better that rate.

Not only did the oysters grow phenomenally fast, but by controlling the calcium content of the water in relation to the mollusks' growth rate, the researchers were able to control the thickness of the animals' shells. For each pound of food that it eats, a thin-shelled oyster produces more meat per pound of its own food than a thick-shelled one—the energy that would otherwise go into building shell goes into making meat instead. Of course, a commercial oyster grower must take care to keep the shells thick enough to prevent them from crushing when the oysters are shipped to market, but this is easily managed. A small proportion of iodine is added to the water to give the oysters their characteristic "ocean" flavor.

The closed-cycle system has other advantages. One is that part of the oyster waste can be fed back to the algae, whereas the rest makes a good garden fertilizer. More significantly, since the system is land-based, it can be used to raise oysters anywhere, even in Arizona or Nebraska, or on the fringes of a big city. Such inland

Plump, meaty oysters raised in the "oyster greenhouse" reach market size in nine months (in nature it takes at least three years) and have twice as much meat as natural oysters of the same total weight.
Sea Grant College Program, University of Delaware

mariculturists could either have seawater shipped in by truck or railroad tank car, or purchase the necessary chemicals and mix their own synthetic seawater.

Clams and mussels also do well under the University of Delaware system. In fact, clams have been found to grow even faster than oysters. Dean Gaither and Dr. Kent Price, director of the Lewes complex, told me that the process is on the verge of becoming commercially practical, and they foresee some day a nationwide shellfish industry much like the poultry industry. They pointed out that oysters are the world's most efficient known producers of protein. They yield up to a ton and a half of usable meat per acre, whereas beef cattle yield only about 330 pounds. Thus the closed-cycle oyster-growing system could do much to alleviate world nutrition problems.

Another project that shows much promise is Dr. Paul Austin's work with chitin. Chitin is a natural substance closely related to cellulose. It forms part of the shells of insects and is also an important component of the shells of crabs and other crustaceans. Crab- and shrimp-packing plants produce large quantities of shells as a waste product. Until recently, the only use for this waste was to grind it up and add it to animal feed. Chitin is a remarkably stable material, chemically speaking, and it will not dissolve in water or ordinary industrial solvents—therefore it could not be converted into useful products.

However, Dr. Austin and his colleagues developed a method for extracting purified chitin cheaply from the ground-up shell waste and then dissolving it in a special acid bath. Once dissolved, the chitin can be restructured, somewhat like nylon or polyester, and turned into strong, pliable, transparent films and filaments. A different chemical treatment turns chitin into chitosan, which is soluble in water.

The potential uses for these products are amazing. Since chitin has been found to promote the healing of wounds, chitin powder may one day be used in medicine. Pharmaceutical companies have already shown interest in it. Since chitin does not irritate living tissue, chitin thread seems a promising material for surgical sutures. Other possible uses are sewing thread and textile fiber (chitin takes dye very well). Chitin's insolubility makes chitin a good material for food-wrapping film, and, since it is nontoxic and does not burn at ordinary cooking temperatures, it seems well suited for oven wrap. Another potential use is in photographic film.

Experiments have shown that chitosan, added to paper, increases its strength and improves its printing quality. Another potential use is as a coagulant to trap impurities in water-treatment and sewage-treatment systems. And both chitin and chitosan in flake form may one day be added to tobacco to reduce the toxic content of the smoke.

Pilot plants on the West Coast and Gulf Coast are already producing about a ton of chitin and chitosan a month for researchers. If the University of Delaware scientists are right, chitin may one day become the basis of an industry on a par with the paper industry. Dean Gaither even foresees the possibility of raising special strains of crustaceans just to keep up with the demand for raw material.

Another project with tremendous future potential is the program for developing salt-tolerant food plants. Many areas of the world can not be used for food production because they lack sufficient fresh water. And water supplies are running low in many of the world's present agricultural areas. Desalinating seawater in the quantities needed would be prohibitively expensive.

However, many areas have ample supplies of brackish

(semisalt) water, and many thousands of acres of desert land lie handy to the seacoast. If food plants could be developed that utilize salt or brackish water, these waste areas could be brought into production.

Delaware is not the only institution working on this program. However, while other institutions are trying to breed salt tolerance into conventional food crops such as tomatoes and grains, Delaware's scientists are taking the other tack, working with nature instead of against it. They are looking for plants that thrive naturally in salt marshes and on beaches, and breeding them selectively for greater food value and productivity. So far the best candidates seem to be certain seed-bearing plants such as spartina grass. Wild beans also show promise. And a fruit-bearer, the wild prickly pear, has done well with the saltiest water the researchers used.

One of the people I talked with was Dr. Billy Glass, who holds a joint appointment in the College of Marine Studies and the Department of Geology. Dr. Glass's research has taken him figuratively from the bottom of the ocean to the moon. The story began back in the 1960's, when he was a graduate student at Lamont-Doherty, working under Bruce Heezen. While mapping sediment

Marine science has many ramifications—this student at the University of Delaware's College of Marine Studies is working on a project to develop salt-tolerant food plants.

College of Marine Studies, University of Delaware

cores from the Antarctic Ocean one day, he was distracted by noise from the paleomagnetism lab next door. Glass poked his head into the lab and asked what was making all the racket. A fellow student pointed to one of the machines, a spinner magnetometer that he had developed to test sediment samples for reversals of terrestrial magnetism.

He invited Glass to give the machine a whirl, so he inserted some of his Antarctic core samples. To his surprise and delight, he found a magnetic reversal there. Later, it occurred to Glass that paleomagnetic dating would be a helpful cross-check for the standard system of dating cold periods by changes in the species of fossil forams.

Looking at cores taken from the sea floor south of Australia, Glass found that tiny glassy spheroids kept getting in the way. At first he did not know what the little foreign objects—all less than a millimeter in diameter—were. A fellow student suggested that they might be tektites. Chemical tests proved that they were, and this led Glass onto a new trail.

Tektites are one of the mystery phenomena of geology. They are thought to be produced by the impact of a large meteorite smashing into the Earth. The energy of the impact melts the ground—according to the current theory—and splashes liquid droplets through the air in all directions. The molten droplets, streamlined by their trip through the air, quickly solidify and drop back to the ground. Usually teardrop-shaped or spheroidal, they range in size from half an inch to four inches. One that Dr. Glass showed me was roughly the size and shape of an egg.

Before Dr. Glass's discovery, tektites were known only from the land, and from only a few areas at that—a belt in the Far East stretching from China across Australia; Czechoslovakia; the Ivory Coast in West Africa; and in Texas, Georgia, and Cape Cod in the United States. The presence of Billy Glass's microtektites in deep-sea sediments raised some knotty questions. How did they get there anyway? The glassy spherules are too lightweight to be thrown through the air—air resistance would stop them in a relatively short distance—and too heavy to be carried along by the wind as dust.

Glass and his colleague began a search of cores from various parts of the Pacific and Indian oceans and found microtektites in a fan-shaped swath whose base was near Madagascar and whose outer edge stretched from Japan down past Australia. All of them were in a sediment layer dated at 700,000 years old. Glass later found more microtektites in the equatorial Atlantic Ocean (1 million years old) and in the Caribbean and Gulf of Mexico (34 million years old).

Mysterious as the origin of the microtektites is, and it still has not been explained, Glass found something even more mysterious—the coincidence of the tektite showers with reversals of the Earth's magnetic field and with massive extinctions of radiolarians. No less than 500 species of the microscopic, one-celled plankton carnivores died out at the time the microtekites were deposited. The connection among the three events is not yet known, but with three out of three tektite falls associated with radical changes in the Earth, it cannot be just chance.

After receiving his Ph.D., Dr. Glass was invited by NASA to study samples of lunar soil. There, too, he found microtektites that looked identical to the ones found on Earth. However, they were quite different in their chemical makeup. Glass had to conclude that, although the moon's microtektites were apparently formed by the same process that shaped those of Earth, they didn't shed any light on the origin of tektites.

At the University of Delaware, Dr. Glass continues his studies of microtektites. He showed me some under a microscope. Illuminated by the microscope light, they glowed like tiny, rough-

This microtektite, magnified 182 times, was recovered from a core sample from the floor of the Atlantic Ocean off the Ivory Coast of Africa.
Sea Grant College Program, University of Delaware

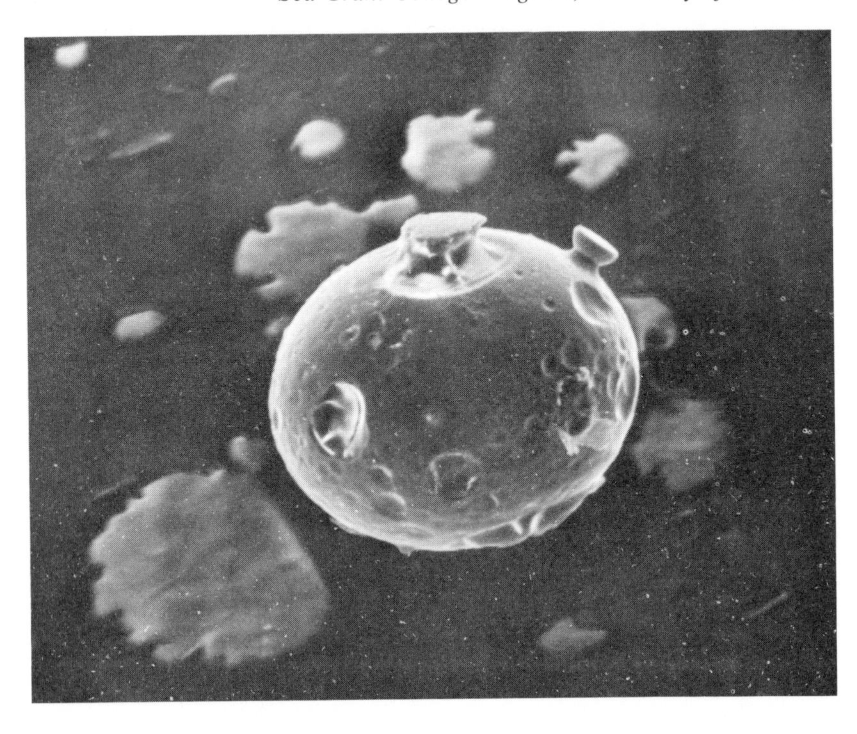

Jewel-like microtektites, magnified twenty-five times, illustrate the diversity of forms these particles of mysterious origin may take.
Sea Grant College Program, University of Delaware

shaped jewels. Perhaps one day he or one of his students will solve the mystery of their origin and their relation to the changes in Earth's magnetic field and the death of the radiolarians. Meanwhile, he is supervising a student who is using fossilized "fish teeth" to corroborate geologic dates on the ocean floor. These "teeth" (in quotes because not all of them are teeth, although they are tooth-shaped) are found in the so-called red clay that carpets much of the ocean floor. They were first found by the *Challenger* expedition in the 1870's, but nothing was done to investigate them until a century later. Dr. Glass's student is currently developing a method for using them in dating.

With research extending from oyster culture to the mysteries of the cosmos, the College of Marine studies will not soon run out of subjects to investigate. And, as Dean Gaither pointed out, there is still a great deal that even the specialists do not know about the ocean in its totality.

12

Virginia Institute of Marine Science

A VIGILANT AGENCY OF THE STATE

A tall, slender bridge carries Route 17 over the York River in the tidewater section of Virginia. At the southern foot of the bridge lie Yorktown and its historic battlefield, where Cornwallis surrendered to George Washington. At the northern foot lie the tiny community of Gloucester Point and the Virginia Institute of Marine Science.

VIMS (pronounced to rhyme with *trims*) occupies a 35-acre campus sloping down to the edge of the river; a few miles away the river opens into Chesapeake Bay, and at Gloucester Point it is salty. Jutting out into the river are the piers where the institute's research vessels lie: the 144-foot *Virginian Sea,* a converted Navy minesweeper; the 80-foot *Langley,* a former auto ferry; the 55-foot trawler *Pathfinder,* a 20-year-old veteran; and a little fleet of smaller vessels. Most of the campus is occupied by laboratory and office buildings. A branch laboratory is located on the Atlantic coast of the Delmarva peninsula at Wachapreague.

VIMS serves as the School of Marine Science of the College of William and Mary, and most of the faculty hold appointments on the William and Mary staff. (For a number of years VIMS also served as the Department of Marine Science of the University of Virginia, but this connection has been terminated.) The director of the institute, Dr. William J. Hargis, Jr., is an articulate, hard-driving perfectionist, acutely conscious of his institution's mission of public service. All the marine-science institutions in the United States, dependent as they are on government funds, do have a service mission, but VIMS's mandate is unique. By state law, it is designated as the official research, investigative, and advisory agency of the Commonwealth of Virginia in all matters relating to marine, estuarine, and coastal areas.

When the kepone scandal broke and an alarmed public learned that massive amounts of the poisonous chemical had been carried down the James River to Chesapeake Bay, VIMS was called on to help assess the danger. When stinging jellyfish clogged fishermen's nets and drove tourists from beach resorts, VIMS was handed the task of finding a means of controlling the unwelcome coelenterates. (No solution has been found yet, but they are still at work on it.) Do beaches need protection from erosion? Do clam growers need advice on preparing the bottom for a new batch of seed clams? VIMS researchers supply the answers.

VIMS has been involved in public service from its very beginning in 1938 as an investigation into oyster problems by the William and Mary biology department. In 1940 this small investigative program burgeoned into the Virginia Fisheries Laboratory, which occupied a few small buildings in Yorktown. The Fisheries Laboratory was supported partly by the College of William and Mary and partly by the state, and in 1943 the hybrid institution granted its first M.S. degree. In 1950 the Yorktown bridge was built, usurping the site of the Fisheries Lab, and the staff and equipment moved across the river to Gloucester Point to a brand-new home in Maury Hall, the main building of VIMS. In 1962 "Doc" Hargis became the institute's director and began expanding its sphere of activities. No longer confined to fisheries work, the institute changed its name to the Virginia Institute of Marine Science. A tough and demanding boss, Hargis gathered around him a team of men who shared his devotion to science—and its application to current problems.

Growth was slow—in 1967 VIMS had only thirty students. But by 1976 it had approximately a hundred, with sixty-six faculty members, plus technical and administrative staff making up a total of nearly five hundred. Dr. Hargis told me that each year he receives applications from two to three hundred qualified students (and many more from unqualified college grads), but can accept only fifteen to thirty. From eight to twelve newly accredited scientists receive their Ph.D.s from VIMS each year.

Because of VIMS' advisory function, its research is coupled very closely to the decision-making process. Since the students work on the research problems their professors have undertaken, they have an unusually intimate contact with decision making on its various levels. And by working with their supervisors every day, they are able to get constant feedback on their progress and their problems.

A unique feature of VIMS is that it has a separate administration from its parent university and is budgeted separately. This helps to maintain the independence of the institution, which is vital to performing its advisory functions impartially and objectively. A case where this independence was manifested was when a power company wished to erect a nuclear plant near Newport News. The company brought pressure to bear on the state legislature and the regulatory bodies, and the construction unions threw in their muscle on the side of the company. The construction of the plant would have created two or three years' worth of jobs, and when in operation it might have brought power rates down slightly. But the danger of contaminating the lower Chesapeake Bay area with nuclear wastes that last for many human lifetimes outweighed the short-term benefits that building the power plant would have yielded. The forceful and well-documented testimony of VIMS' experts was instrumental in preventing the construction of the plant.

A student analyzes chlorophyll content of a sample.
Virginia Institute of Marine Science

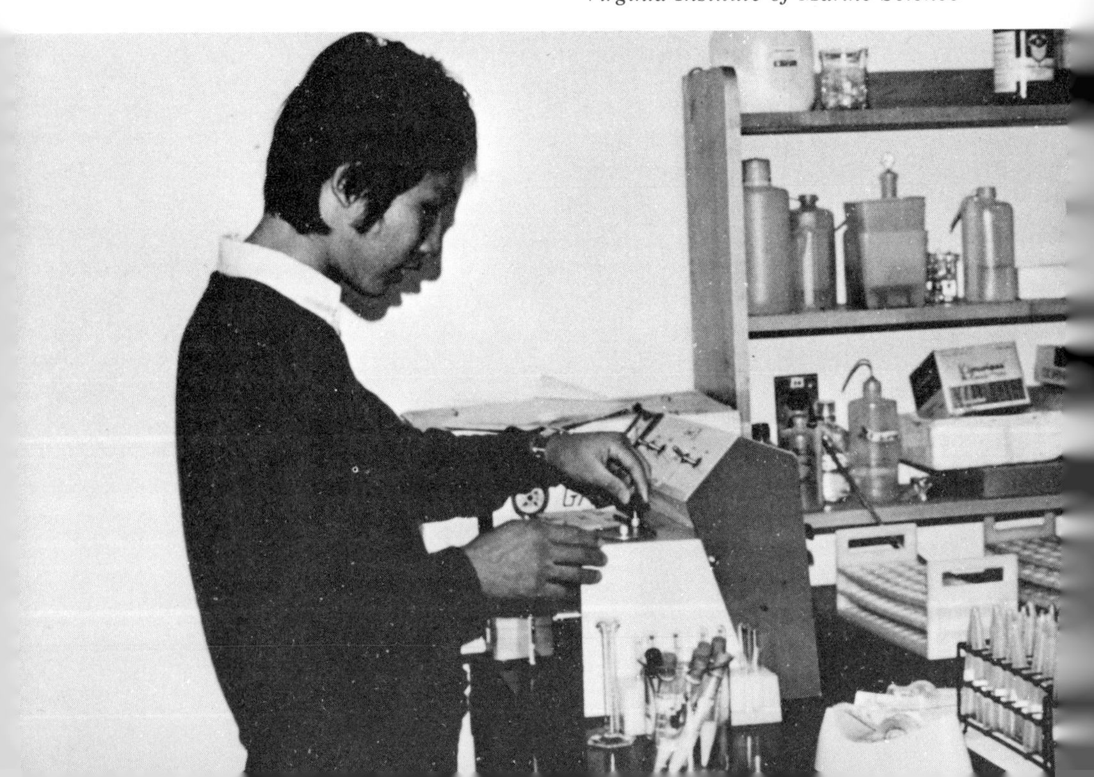

At the time I visited VIMS, over two hundred projects were in progress. Most of these were directed at solving specific goals, for the institute's philosophy calls for a purposeful, multidisciplinary, directed research program. It is not all directed, however. Some of the scientists pursue independent research, such as studies of coral reefs in the South Pacific and shoreline erosion work in Central and South America. Their colleagues find applications for the discoveries these independents make.

At a time when most oceanographic institutions were competing in deep-water investigations, VIMS made the conscious decision to specialize in coastal and estuarine work ("coastal" includes the continental shelf out to its edge). As a result, VIMS is now in the forefront of coastal and estuarine research at a period when the action is shifting away from the deep sea to the coastal areas. Dr. Hargis told me that VIMS is now the largest coastally oriented institution in the United States, with an operating budget of nearly $7 million.

VIMS claims as its area of operations the "Virginian Sea," a grandiose appellation for the water between Cape Cod and Cape Hatteras. Most of VIMS' work, however, is done between Cape Hatteras and Cape May, New Jersey, with particular emphasis on Chesapeake Bay and its tributaries. In 1972 its resources were concentrated on finding and recording the effects of tropical storm Agnes, which forced massive quantities of water into the Chesapeake estuary. Another year, the target project was a gigantic fish kill that left the waters of the Chesapeake littered with the floating carcasses of dead fish. The finding here was that the fish had been poisoned by chlorine in the discharges of sewage plants, the first documented case of heavy fish kills by chlorinated water.

In 1976 VIMS' target was the kepone in Chesapeake Bay, a mission of the greatest urgency. Chemical and physical oceanographers joined forces with biologists and geologists to track the kepone and assess its effects. By analyzing sediments and biological samples they were able to establish how far the poisonous chemical had moved up the bay from the mouth of the James River, how far tidal movements had carried it up the various river mouths that open into the bay, and in what way it had entered into the food web. Other questions the VIMS team is looking into include these: What happens to the kepone when it is absorbed by sediments? What chemical changes does it undergo, if any? How deep in the sediments does it penetrate? What happens to it in the bodies of marine animals? How long does it take to break down, and what does it turn into? (Some breakdown products of toxic chemicals are just as poisonous as the original product.) How much kepone do fish and other marine animals absorb from their food, and how much from the water? How much kepone is likely to be transported in the bodies of migrating fish? How much by currents?

I was introduced to Bob Huggett, the hard-working oceanographer who coordinates the chemical work on kepone. I found him surrounded by gas chromatographs and other sophisticated analytical machinery. The chatter of a computer printer almost drowned out our conversation, but Bob was able to tell me some of the problems he and his colleagues have faced. One of them is the fact that kepone reacts differently in the environment than do the other chlorinated hydrocarbons, because its molecules contain oxygen, whereas the others do not. Thus, new tests had to be devised. More than a thousand samples of marine life and sediments had been analyzed already, and some important answers were beginning to emerge: There is not much magnification as kepone moves up the food chain. Oysters get rid of their kepone content rapidly and do not take up as much as fish. Fish retain their kepone for a long time; however, some fish take up kepone less rapidly than others. It also appears probable that seafood is the only source of kepone in the human diet.

Another side of the operations of a marine-science institution was revealed when I met Dr. John Zeigler, director of the geological, chemical, and physical oceanography programs at VIMS. When I walked into his office, Dr. Zeigler was working on a contract proposal for the EPA (Environmental Protection Agency). Ninety percent of the funds in his department, he explained, come from outside work. This particular contract covered a study of Chesapeake Bay and would involve $400,000 of federal money to pay for surveys and analyses.

Sediment samples were to be taken from 1,200 stations throughout the bay, then analyzed for sediment characteristics, pesticides, heavy metals, organic compounds, and nutrients. Seismic profiling would reveal the location of the various subsurface layers; where each layer approached the surface of the bottom, a core sample would be taken. The work would be divided among VIMS, the main branch of William and Mary, the University of Maryland, the Maryland Geological Survey, Old Dominion University, and EPA personnel. Each outfit would contribute its specialties to the whole study. The University of Maryland, for instance, would undertake the heavy-metals analysis. VIMS, whose organic-chemistry lab is rated among the finest on the East Coast, would do the organic analyses. EPA would carry out the pesticide tests, Old Dominion the nutrient analyses, and so on. A formidable diagram on the blackboard behind Dr. Zeigler's desk showed the intricacies of the proposed operating structure.

Dr. Zeigler was reviewing two other proposals concurrently. One, involving the operation of a new hydraulic model of Chesapeake Bay, was to be carried out by the Chesapeake Research Consortium, a group that includes Johns Hopkins University, the University of Maryland, and the Smithsonian Institution, as well as VIMS. Although VIMS would have only a minor role in this particular operation, Dr. Zeigler took on the task of writing up the proposal because the project would benefit Virginia. He applies two tests in evaluating a proposal: (1) Will it benefit the Commonwealth of Virginia? and (2) Can VIMS handle it?

VIMS regards its students as practicing researchers who are learning on the job rather than as novices who have to be trained. Zeigler extends his students' expertise to coping with bureaucracy as well as with science. Under his direction, they fill out forms and prepare cost estimates that will go to the various agencies with which VIMS deals, a highly practical addition to their education.

From the head of the Division of Biological Oceanography, Dr. Maurice Lynch, a transplanted Bostonian, I learned about the baseline studies that VIMS is conducting on the continental shelf for the Bureau of Land Management. A baseline study is designed to learn the conditions that prevail in a particular area (such as the amount of pollution present in water and sediments, the patterns of currents and water circulation, and the animals and plants that inhabit the area) before man changes these conditions by some new activity such as filling in coastal wetlands, building an oil port, or dredging sand and gravel from the ocean floor. These particular baseline studies are part of the BLM's environmental assessment program linked to exploration for oil and gas off the coast of the middle Atlantic states.

The largest single project at VIMS, the baseline study, is funded at approximately $3 million a year. Interdisciplinary by its very nature, it involves the skills and experience of biologists, chemists, geologists, and physical oceanographers. Their mission includes an extensive analysis of hydrocarbons and trace metals in the environment. They seek these substances in sediments, benthos (bottom-dwelling animals), zooplankton, neuston (surface-dwelling plankton), and suspended material in the water. In addition, the relationships of the different benthic animals to one another and their environment are being examined, along with their condition of health or disease. One task force of scientists is studying the bacteria found in the water and sediments.

Samples are taken four times a year, over the entire shelf area from northern New Jersey to northern Virginia, using VIMS' own research vessels and larger ships chartered from other institutions or private companies. The sampling program, begun in 1975, is expected to continue into 1979 or 1980 before the baseline is established.

Of all the OCS (Outer Continental Shelf) environmental-study programs, only this one is being carried out essentially by a single institution. Thanks to its size, capabilities, and directed programming, VIMS was a logical choice.

Tidewater Virginia is one of the nation's major commercial oyster-producing areas, and one of VIMS' ongoing programs is oyster genetics. Dr. John Dupuy and his associates have been working since 1968 on breeding oysters for faster growth, a good shape, and resistance to MSX, the disease that nearly wiped out the oyster industry in Delaware Bay.

MSX (short for Multinucleated Spore of Unknown Nature) was thought for years to be a fungus. It is now classed as a protozoan and called *Minchinia nelsoni.* Regardless of its classification, it is deadly to most oysters. It first appeared in Delaware Bay in 1957 and within two years had wiped out most of the oysters in that region. Marine biologists learned that MSX did not thrive in water of low salt content, so they were able to prevent a great deal of loss in Chesapeake Bay by mapping low-salt areas and advising oyster growers to plant their seed stock there. However, this meant abandoning large areas of productive oyster bottom. And oysters that live in low-salinity water grow more slowly and are less flavorful than oysters raised in high-salinity water. The solution was to create an oyster with high resistance to MSX, and this the VIMS team achieved.

Attacking from another front, they aimed for an oyster that would grow to market size in two years (young oysters are much less susceptible to MSX than those over two years old). They also bred in traits for desirable shape. Dr. Dupuy explained that a well-shaped oyster has a deeply cupped left valve (shell half), which means more meat per oyster, and a flattened right valve, which is good for the half-shell trade. Unfortunately, they found that after five generations of inbreeding, their oysters lost MSX-resistance, so they had to back-cross and create new strains. The results were not yet known at the time of my visit.

Another genetic program was crossing the huge Japanese oyster, *Crassostrea gigas,* with the native American oyster. The goal was to achieve an oyster with faster growth and greater hardiness. But before these hybrids can be released to growers, the VIMS researchers must learn whether or not they can reproduce themselves outside the laboratory. If they are sterile, hatchery-reared hybrids may be the base of a new industry. If they are fertile, the law will prohibit their release into the open water, for fear that the

Inspecting oyster beds is one of the tasks to which VIMS students may be assigned.
Virginia Institute of Marine Science

exotic species will crowd out the native ones.

The oyster-hatchery program was another VIMS project. Working with a pilot model, VIMS researchers demonstrated that oysters could be induced to spawn on a year-round basis by controlling the temperature and nutrient content of the water. The process is now used commercially by an oyster hatchery in Maryland. An important part of the program was developing an improved mix of algae for the oyster larvae to feed on, thus cutting the time required for setting them out from two weeks to nine days. Over a year, this time saving can mean close to ten extra batches of seed oysters. Rounding out the oyster program, VIMS engineers developed a mechanical oyster harvester.

VIMS has also worked on techniques for growing hard clams and scallops—much of this work has been done at the Wachapreague branch. The biologists found that covering the bottom with crushed shell or fine gravel before setting out the baby clams gave them an excellent cover for hiding from predators such as the oyster drill. They found also that 25 to 50 clams per square foot is the optimum number for planting. Overcrowding causes the clams to move away from each other; many will leave the protected area and fall victim to predators.

A good deal of attention has been given to methods of handling blue crabs while waiting for them to molt their shells. Crabs that show signs of molting are held in tanks until they lose their shells, then removed before their hard-shelled tankmates can destroy them. Softshell crabs are in great demand as a seafood delicacy, while the demand for "peeler" crabs—those in the last stages before molting—for fish bait is even greater. VIMS is also exploring possible commercial uses for other local crab species such as the rock crab, the jonah crab, and the red crab, as yet hardly touched by commercial fisheries.

Yet another VIMS program is beach protection. It is a perennial problem because beaches are always being worn away by erosion. In storms, they can disappear alarmingly fast. Since Virginia has some 5,000 miles of shoreline and a marine-recreation industry worth millions of dollars, its beaches are important to the state. The traditional solutions for beach erosion are seawalls (easily undermined by waves), riprap (a covering of heavy rocks that does not make for a comfortable beach), or groins, which are jetties that stick out from the shore and deflect the current. Groins work well in some situations, but it often turns out that the groin which protects your beach causes the next person's stretch of beach to wash out.

VIMS developed a simple device called a *sill,* made of big plastic bags filled with sand. Anchored parallel to the shore a short distance below the low-water line, the sills trap sand behind them and actually build the beach up. Natural vegetation takes root and helps to consolidate the beach.

This is definitely applied research. In a more basic field, VIMS' physical oceanographers worked out a computer model of wave-height distributions along the shore from Cape Hatteras to Cape Henlopen. The model is expected to see heavy use as plans are made for offshore oil exploration, development of deep-water ports, and possibly floating, offshore nuclear-power plants. VIMS scientists have also studied the effects of the heated discharges from a nuclear-power plant on the James River and have worked with the state Division of Water Resources to develop a mathematical model of all Virginia's estuaries. Dr. Zeigler pointed out that a mathematical model is much cheaper to create than an actual physical model, and gives the answers faster. However, VIMS does operate a physical model of the James River at a U.S. Army Corps of Engineers lab at Vicksburg, Mississippi.

Education is another service VIMS provides to the Commonwealth of Virginia. Groups from schools and colleges make regular guided tours to the labs and the small but well-stocked museum and aquariums. In the warmer months, VIMS staffers take them out in the field for collecting expeditions. VIMS' research vessels take out school groups when they are not needed for gathering data. VIMS also helps schools to develop marine-education programs, sends lecturers to speak at schools, and maintains an extensive lending collection of films and film strips. The institution also publishes informational pamphlets and advisory bulletins, and its 20,000-volume library is available to seekers of technical information. A National Marine Education Materials Service is currently being developed for teachers who wish to add a salty flavor to their classes. There are also short summer training courses for elementary and high-school teachers, and college groups can arrange to use the facilities for field work.

In its capacity of advisory service, VIMS acts as adviser to the Potomac River Fisheries Commission, the Atlantic States Marine Fisheries Commission, the Coastal States Organization, and other bodies. VIMS faculty members sit on the boards of NACOA (National Advisory Committee for Oceans and Atmosphere) and simular bodies. The Marine Environment and Resources Research and Management System keeps an ever-growing collection of marine-research data from all over the United States and makes it available to anyone who needs it.

To steal a line from Dr. Hargis, it looks as if VIMS will be in business for a long time solving tomorrow's problems today.

13

Duke University Marine Laboratory

A SMALL INSTITUTION THAT SERVES A LARGE CONSTITUENCY

On the windswept coast of North Carolina, about halfway between Woods Hole, Massachusetts, and Miami, Florida, is the Duke University Marine Laboratory. The institution is built on one end of Pivers Island, a 25-acre pile of sand held in place by a concrete seawall. Pivers Island lies only 150 yards offshore from the little town of Beaufort, best known as a fishing port and summer resort. The coastline is low and sandy, pierced by what seem like hundreds of creeks and estuaries over which traffic passes on high-arched, humpbacked bridges. Off the shore, and connected to the mainland by causeways, lie the long low islands of the Outer Banks. Wherever these are not protected by federal or state parks, they have degenerated into replicas of the overcrowded resorts of the Jersey shore.

The Duke University Marine Laboratory, usually abbreviated as DUML, was founded in 1938 to house a summer training program for Duke seniors and graduate students who planned to enter science-teaching careers. Soon the first research programs, small and tentative, were launched. The next step in the Duke Marine Lab's growth was broadening its scope to accept students from other schools, but it remained a summer institute until the mid-1950's, when the first year-round programs were instituted. Today, DUML somehow accommodates a year-round graduate program, an active summer program, a spring program for undergraduates, and several international training programs. The director, Dr. John D. Costlow, is a large, imposing man with a deep, booming voice, who struck me as a man who combines strong opinions with an open mind.

DUML is unusual in many ways. Although a respected marine-science institution, it grants no degrees and is not even a university department in its own right. It is an interdepartmental research facility of Duke University, representing the departments of biology, zoology, botany, biochemistry, chemistry, and geology. Graduate students are enrolled in one of these departments. They do their research and some of their course work at the Marine Lab, but they get their degrees from the departments at the main campus in Durham.

At present, DUML has about sixteen graduate students and fourteen resident faculty. It turns out about two Ph.D. graduates a year. As we said, it is a small institution. But it more than makes up for its size by the amazing diversity of programs it conducts. The summer program, which accommodates students from other universities, gives a basic grounding in biological oceanography, as well as courses in chemical and geological oceanography. The spring term for undergraduates, usually taken in the junior year, gives science students an exposure to the broad field of the marine sciences so that they can decide if marine science is really their field of choice. If it is, they can begin specializing in their senior year; if not, they avoid the possibility of wasting two years in graduate school before they discover that marine science is not what they want to do after all. Lastly—and Dr. Costlow considers it very important—the spring program broadens the perspectives of the students and gives them an awareness of the environment and its fragility.

The laboratory also makes its facilities available to groups from other colleges and universities that lack their own marine facilities. Dr. Costlow told me that hundreds of marine-science students around the nation had their first exposure to oceanography at sea aboard DUML's research vessels. Another innovative program, funded by the Rockefeller Foundation and UNESCO, brings groups of scientists from developing countries to DUML for intensive two-month courses in such newly vital skills as monitoring oil pollution of their coastal waters. Through those scientists, the influence of Duke reaches around the world.

The cooperative approach dates from the early 1960's, when DUML's second director, Dr. C. G. Bookhout, secured a $1.9 million grant from the National Science Foundation to establish a program in oceanography. It may not have been entirely altruistic. Dr. Bookhout knew that Duke could not support an oceanographic program on its own, and the chances of getting the grant were much improved by offering to share equipment, facilities, and knowledge with other schools. The sharing extended to Duke's then-new research vessel *Eastward,* built in 1964. Concerned that Duke might get more than its fair share of ship time, the conscientious Bookhout set up a seven-man panel to evaluate applications for the use of the ship and allocate ship time according to merit—the forerunner of UNOLS (University-National Oceanographic Laboratory Systems). Only one member of the panel was from Duke; the rest were from other interested institutions.

The *Eastward* was designed expressly for gathering biological oceanographic data. Originally planned as a 125-footer, it ended up at 117½ feet when funds ran low. This slight shrinkage did not cripple the ship's effectiveness, however. "The *Eastward* can take the sea," quipped Bookhout, "whether the people aboard can or not." And in truth the *Eastward* has the reputation of being an uncomfortable ship.

With a cruising range of a thousand miles and fourteen days, the *Eastward* does a good deal of coring and other geological work as well as biology, plus a minor amount of chemical sampling. No physical oceanographic investigation is done, primarily because the necessary equipment is too expensive.

One hundred feet down off the coast of North Carolina, blue angelfish hover by a natural rock outcropping encrusted with hydroids, sponges, and soft corals. The photo is part of a National Marine Fisheries Service study of food and game fish communities along the continental shelf.

National Marine Fisheries Service

The region around Beaufort is practically designed by nature for marine biologists. The warm Gulf Stream meets a cold coastal current just offshore, and southern and northern species of sea life mingle to yield an extraordinarily rich variety. It was for this reason that Dr. A. S. Pearse, the founder of DUML, chose this place for his laboratory. Pearse was the head of Duke's zoology department, and his two successors, Bookhout and Costlow, have continued the lab's strong emphasis on biological investigation.

An outstanding achievement was the success of the team of Bookhout and Costlow in raising the commercially important blue crab in the laboratory from its larval stages to maturity. This breakthrough, which was accomplished in 1959, has been described as a milestone in marine biology. It made it possible to conduct continuous investigations ranging from changes in the crab's physiology and behavior as it grows to the effects on it of various chemical pollutants. Some of the most important work on the effects of pesticides on shellfish has come out of DUML.

A current program investigates the effects of juvenile-hormone pesticides (used to control insects) on crustaceans. So far, said Dr. Costlow, the hormones do not appear to have harmed commercially important crustaceans such as crabs—an overdose will kill them, but lesser doses do not prevent them from maturing. On the other hand, not much is known about their effects on the more primitive crustaceans such as copepods, which form an important part of the ocean food chain.

One interesting finding is that one of the synthetic juvenile-hormone pesticides interferes with the development of barnacles. But instead of keeping the barnacles forever in the larval stage, it makes them mature too rapidly, which results in stunted, malformed juvenile barnacles with a low rate of survival into adulthood and reproduction. This could conceivably lead to a chemical method of keeping ships' hulls free of barnacles. It also illustrates the unexpected consequences of man's introducing new substances into the environment.

Dr. Costlow has been involved in studying the ways in which hormones regulate the development of crab larvae. One aspect is the regeneration of lost or injured parts. Another is the hormonal control of molting. Conceivably this could be used some day by seafood dealers to ensure a year-round supply of soft-shell crabs, but DUML is looking for basic understanding rather than commercial applications.

Most of DUML's research is done on invertebrates or very low vertebrates (low on the evolutionary scale, that is). Many basic concepts of physiology have been discovered in these lowly animals and later applied to human medicine. Enzymatic reactions

National Marine Service personnel from the NOAA lab at Beaufort, North Carolina, wash plankton from a stainless-steel net into a collecting cup.
National Marine Fisheries Service

and embryonic development are examples. (It should be pointed out that such studies are done all over the world, and that they began long before DUML was founded.)

One of the resident biologists at DUML is William Kirby-Smith, a great-grandson of the famous Confederate general. Kirby-Smith is investigating what he calls "the energetics of the interactions between vegetarian filter-feeders such as the bay scallop and the phytoplankton present in their ambient water." Translated into layman's language, this means "How fast do the shellfish grow at different temperatures and with different concentrations of food?" He has found that adding extra food to the scallops' water does not make them grow faster. They are equipped to assimilate only as much as they encounter under natural conditions. Although Dr. Kirby-Smith was not looking for practical applications for his research, this information is of value to commercial scallop growers.

Dr. Kirby-Smith would also like to investigate what causes northern mussels to die when transplanted to southern waters. The mussels do all right in winter, but in the hot season they perish. The conventional explanation is heat shock, but Kirby-Smith suspects that the animals actually starve to death when the high water temperature kicks their metabolism into high gear, and they burn up their food faster than they can take it in.

But this scientist's work is not limited to "pure" research.

Another of his projects is measuring the effects of cow manure on the local estuarine ecosystem. A large corporate cattle-ranching firm bought up a tract of pine barrens and swamp, cleared it, dug drainage ditches, and converted it to pasture. Could the nutrient-rich drainage choke the salt marshes and coastal shallows with a rank overgrowth of vegetation and kill them? So far, the results have been reassuring. But, like every other alteration of the ecosystem, warned Kirby-Smith, it needs continuous, long-term monitoring.

Systematics ecology is an ongoing program at DUML. The Duke researchers concentrate on algae, seaweeds, and phytoplankton—the base of the food chain. Eventually they will have enough data to create a computer model of what happens when man disturbs a marine community by, say, dumping dredging spoil or releasing heated cooling water from a power plant.

On another level, biochemists Joseph Bonaventura, his wife, Celia, and Bo Sullivan are working on hemoglobin and other respiratory pigments. All holders of the Ph.D., these scientists belong to the Duke Medical School, and their work is funded by the American Heart Association.

The Bonaventuras work chiefly with fish hemoglobins. Joe Bonaventura began by telling me that hemoglobin is the most thoroughly studied and best-known protein there is, yet no one knows for certain how it works. He went on to explain that there are hundreds of types of hemoglobin, each one having a different molecular structure and different properties that depend on the structure. Man has only one kind of hemoglobin in his red blood cells, but fishes have a number of different kinds in theirs, each with a different function. One type, for instance, gives up its oxygen very easily. Its job, apparently, is to keep the fish's swim bladder filled with gas. Another type absorbs oxygen readily and keeps the swim bladder from being pumped too full and exploding the fish. One day fish hemoglobins may be used as a biological oxygen pump to keep divers supplied with oxygen.

Another possibility mentioned by Dr. Bonaventura was tailoring the hemoglobin of human blood cells to alter its oxygen-carrying capacity. He spoke of creating a hemoglobin with low oxygen affinity for use in hospitals. The low affinity means that the hemoglobin gives up its oxygen easily, which might save the life of a struggling patient. Another of his objectives is to find some way of treating sickle-cell anemia, the disease that kills thousands of Negroes every year while they are still young. Sickle-cell anemia is caused by a malformed hemoglobin, and Dr. Bonaventura hopes to find some way of altering the hemoglobin back to a normal structure.

Hemoglobins are not the only respiratory pigments in the ani-

In the lab, a student records data. *Duke University Marine Laboratory*

mal kingdom. There is another class of red oxygen carriers called the hemerythrins, which exist only in a few kinds of primitive organisms, such as tube worms. There are also the hemocyanins, blue pigments based on copper instead of iron, which are found in the blood of crabs, lobsters, and other crustaceans. Hemocyanin molecules are much larger and more complex than hemoglobin molecules and give a scientist much more to investigate. Dr. Bonaventura works with hemocyanins from horsehoe crabs. These animals live in shallow offshore waters where the temperature and salinity are constantly fluctuating. It is thought that the complex hemocyanin molecules help the crabs cope with their constantly changing environment, and the Bonaventuras would like to find out how.

The equipment in oceanographic laboratories is pretty much standard: electron microscopes, gas chromatographs, computers, and other sophisticated devices, all necessary for the kind of work they do. But Dr. Bonaventura has one device that is worth special mention. It measures the capacity of hemoglobin for retaining oxygen and carbon monoxide, and it works by the energy of light. A charge of very high-voltage electricity is sent through a specially designed argon lamp, and the resulting intense flash is focused on the sample of gas-saturated hemoglobin. The terrific jolt of light energy knocks the gas molecules loose so that they can be measured.

Along with its specialized biological programs, DUML has a broad oceanographic program. One of the chief current projects is a study of the ecosystems produced by upwelling of nutrient-rich deep water. DUML investigators are participating in CUEA (Coastal Upwelling Ecosystems Analysis), a cooperative program that studies the upwelling off the northwest coast of Africa. They are also investigating upwelling in the Caribbean and off the coast of Peru. In fact, at the time of my visit, the *Eastward* was taking samples in Peruvian waters. Another project involves studying how phytoplankton organisms (plankton plants) condition the water around them by substances they secrete. It is thought that this conditioning has a favorable effect on animal plankton, too. Other investigations include the chemical reactions that take place in upwelling ecosystems and their effect on the biological productivity, and the rate at which sewage sludge is recycled by marine organisms. Geological investigations are mainly focused on the sediments of the continental shelf; how they get there, and how they are distributed.

DUML has a close working relationship with the NOAA Beaufort Laboratory, formerly the Atlantic Estuarine Fisheries Center, which shares Pivers Island with Duke. Though scientists from the two labs seldom do joint investigations, they use one another's facilities quite freely. The NOAA laboratory was originally founded in 1899 as a federal fisheries laboratory, the second oldest in the country. In addition to its work in fishery research, it now conducts an ecological program. From the late 1950's to the early 1970's, the lab was one of the centers for the study of the uptake of radioactive substances in the marine food web.

The fisheries program is concerned primarily with menhaden, a small, herringlike fish of tremendous importance as a source of oil and animal feed. In fact, menhaden is the principal item in the United States annual catch. The NOAA researchers sample commercial catches, conduct surveys of young fish, and tag fishes to follow their life history. They study age and growth rates, conduct in-depth analyses of menhaden stocks, and predict their annual abundance. They are also working with fisheries groups from the Atlantic and Gulf states on management plans to prevent the overexploitation of this valuable resource. Another program involves such important sport-fishing species as snappers, groupers, and other fishes that inhabit reef outcroppings along the edge of the continental shelf.

The ecological program involves a wide range of subjects. One of the prime ones is the effects of energy-related activities on fishery productivity, particularly in coastal and estuarine areas. "Energy-related activities" translates into offshore oil drilling, offshore and coastal power plants, and refineries located on the coast. A part of this research program traces the movement of heavy metals and other contaminants through the food web, and also determines the effects of high temperatures on marine animals. One interesting finding is that copper, one of the most toxic metals, is apparently less poisonous close to shore than out at sea. The reason is that the organic materials from land runoff, etc., which are plentiful in inshore water, tend to neutralize copper ions by binding them up in complex compounds. But out at sea the water is poor in these organic substances, so more of the copper ions stay free. Thus a given weight of copper is more poisonous in the open ocean. Cadmium, on the other hand, does not bind to organic substances but forms strong bonds with chloride ions. Thus a given weight of cadmium is more toxic in the less saline waters close to shore and less toxic in the strongly saline water of the open sea.

The NOAA lab studies basic principles, not specific cases, and its scientists may serve as expert witnesses on the probable consequences of man-made environmental alterations, such as the construction of a power plant in an estuarine area. It also has a close link with North Carolina State University. Several Beaufort Lab scientists serve on the North Carolina State faculty, and graduate students from the university do their research at the NOAA facility. Students from other schools also do research there, including the University of Virginia and Oregon State University.

The Duke lab and the NOAA lab are two members of a marine-research complex. The other members are located in Morehead City, two bridges and a couple of traffic lights away from Pivers Island. East Carolina State University has a seafood technology institute; the State of North Carolina has a marine fisheries division; and the University of North Carolina maintains its Institute of Marine Sciences. I was fortunate enough to talk to the IMS' director, Dr. Alphonse Chestnut, a courtly Rutgers graduate who has held that post since 1955. Dr. Chestnut told me that the IMS is purely a research institution. It does no teaching, although University of North Carolina students come down to do their research there. The seven resident scientists are tenured members of the UNC faculty, although they have no teaching load.

The IMS, like its neighbors, concentrates on biological research. It was formally opened in 1948, on a former naval base, with the mandate of serving the fishing industry. The first research programs, on shrimps, scallops, and oysters, were to be based on knowledge gathered in other parts of the country. However, Dr. Chestnut told me, the IMS scientists soon found that they had to go into basic research to learn why things were the way they were. Information that held true of oysters in New England and shrimps in Louisiana, for example, did not apply to oysters and shrimps off the Carolina coast.

In past years the IMS has done pesticide studies, monitored the setting intensity of oyster larvae, and investigated marine fungi, to mention a few of its many research programs. A current program is a study of the interface where the water meets the sediments of the bottom. Here dwells a specialized community of animals, plants, and one-celled organisms.

Like DUML, the IMS opens its facilities to groups of students from other institutions. Many of these visiting researchers, after they go on to teach at other schools, return to do further research in their specialties. Some send their own students down in turn, maintaining the continuity of relationships that seems to be a strong characteristic of the marine sciences.

DUML personnel lower an underwater camera for studies of benthic (bottom-dwelling) fauna.

Duke University Marine Laboratory

14

The Rosenstiel School

A CENTER OF TROPICAL RESEARCH

Ranked by many as Number Four in American marine research, the Rosenstiel School of Marine and Atmospheric Science is located on the flat coral islet of Virginia Key, just off the Florida mainland and the city of Miami. It shares the island with NOAA's Atlantic Oceanographic and Meteorological Laboratories, the Southeast Fisheries Center (also NOAA), the International Oceanographic Foundation, and the Miami Seaquarium. Dade County and the City of Miami, which share the ownership of the Key, plan to dedicate it entirely to marine and atmospheric research and education.

The Rosenstiel School, a division of the University of Miami, began its existence in 1943 as the university's Marine Laboratory. Under the guidance of its director, a peppery little Englishman named F. G. Walton Smith, the Marine Laboratory expanded after World War II into the Institute of Marine Science. One of its earliest successes, in 1947, was identifying the organism that was causing a severe epidemic of "red tide" in the Gulf of Mexico and killing millions of fish—a one-celled dinoflagellate, *Gymnodinium brevis*. Dr. Smith and his team scored another success with research on marine borers, which do hundreds of thousands of dollars' worth of damage annually to wooden pilings and boat hulls in warm waters like those off Miami. This was followed by a series of studies on conservation measures for the saltwater game fish that lure thousands of free-spending sportsmen to Florida. This record of accomplishment helped to attract support for the young institution and its programs.

In 1969, with a large grant from the Rosenstiel Foundation, the institute became the Dorothy H. and Lewis Rosenstiel School of Marine and Atmospheric Science. For convenience, the lengthy title is usually abbreviated to RSMAS, which those in the know pronounce "Rasmus."

Dr. Smith retired as dean of RSMAS in 1973 but continues to take an active interest in the development of the school. He also has the full-time job of running the International Oceanographic Foundation.

One of the reasons for the original founding of RSMAS was the need for a tropical marine station in the mainland United States. The school has continued to specialize in tropical oceanography and marine science. Among its major subjects of study are the Gulf Stream, the geology of the Florida-Bahama limestone plateau and of the island arc formed by the Antilles, and the ecology of the coastal waters. RSMAS investigators also study the ecology of the Everglades-Florida Bay region.

One recent project was a study of the benthic (bottom-dwelling) fish populations of the Tongue of the Ocean, a deep gash that penetrates the shallow limestone plateau on which the Bahamas sit. The study, which was a population census as well as a listing of species, was the most intensive study of deep-sea fish communities undertaken to that date. Most of the evidence was gathered by trawling, but two scientists also made eleven dives in the submersible *Alvin* to see whether the actual fish population corresponded with what the trawls were bringing up. (It did.)

I spoke with Dr. Jon Staiger, a biological oceanographer who took part in the dives, one of which went to a depth of 12,019 feet. He counted the fish, studied their distribution—they tended to occur in patches—watched their behavior, and tried to learn whether each species preferred a particular kind of bottom. He made no startling new discoveries, but he did see some quite unexpected phenomena. For example, the beam of the sub's searchlight picked up some fishes of species that were believed to spend all their time sitting on the bottom or swimming just above it—but these fishes were hovering in the water twenty-five or thirty feet above the bottom, feeding on plankton.

On one cruise, the *Alvin's* role was cut short after only three dives, due to mechanical failures. As Dr. Staiger explained, an oceanographer must always make allowance in his plans for

Alvin returns to its mother ship, *Lulu*, after carrying Rosenstiel School scientists on a dive in a submarine canyon in the Bahamas. Support divers leap into the water to guide *Alvin* into the sheltered docking well between *Lulu*'s catamarans.
Rosenstiel School of Marine and Atmospheric Science

breakdowns and bad weather, and he deplored the habits of certain scientists who arrive on board the research vessel with a mountain of gear and plans that would take three or four times the length of the cruise to complete. As chief scientist on many voyages, he had often encountered that problem.

Returning to the topic of submersibles, he made the point that many scientists had been turned off by the heavy use of these underwater research vessels for publicity and promotion in the 1960's. Dives that had been scheduled for research were often canceled so that the sub could take journalists or Navy brass on an undersea joyride. This, he thought, was almost as much a factor as the lack of funds in limiting the use of submersibles in scientific investigation. He mentioned also the great improvements in underwater TV cameras and sonic equipment that made it unnecessary to send down a live observer in all but exceptional cases. Even so, he admitted, what he saw down there on the ocean floor was so exciting that he forgot the discomfort of spending eight hours cooped up in a cramped, chilly metal sphere.

A biologist of quite another kind is Dr. Arthur Myrberg, whose specialty is fish behavior. For twelve years he and his associates have been investigating sharks and their responses to stimuli. One of these scientists studied the visual systems of sharks, discovering that not only do sharks have excellent eyesight; they also have a dual photoreceptor system in each eye, one for bright light and one for dim light. Dr. Myrberg himself has concentrated on sharks' responses to sound.

When I asked him if this research had any application to shark attacks on swimmers, he explained that that was applied research, while he was involved in basic research. What he was looking for were answers to some essential questions: Do sharks perceive sound? Do they respond to it? If they do respond, what kinds of sound cause them to respond in certain ways?

For all their toughness and tenacity of life in the sea, sharks are very fragile when brought into the lab. Only a few species can survive under lab conditions, and then for practical reasons these are almost always young, small specimens. To study large, adult sharks you must go out in the field, which in this case is the open sea. That is what Dr. Myrberg did. Working in a wet suit and scuba rig, he played tape-recorded sounds to the sharks and filmed a record of their reactions. He worked mostly at or near the surface, although on occasion he went as deep as sixty feet. He always kept an antishark cage in the water as a refuge, but he and his associates spent most of their time out in the open, following the sharks about. In twelve years he had no accidents, although he had a few scary moments.

"I have great respect for sharks," he said, "and I have fear of them. They are nothing to play around with. But they are definitely not mysterious. They are animals like any others."

What has he learned from twelve years of studying the sharks? One of Dr. Myrberg's findings is that sharks as a group respond well to underwater sound, particularly sounds of low frequency. The sharks' hearing range extends from 7 or 8 cycles per second to about 1,000 cycles per second. (Human hearing, in contrast, detects sounds between 15 or 16 and 20,000 cycles per second.)

Sharks can orient themselves rapidly to a source of sound and home in on it with great speed. However, Dr. Myrberg found, not all types of sounds attract them. To excite the interest of a shark, the sound must be low-frequency (around 10 cycles per second), sufficiently intense for the shark to detect, continuous, and rapidly pulsed. A sudden, brief sound tends to startle sharks and make them back off for another look at the situation. Irregular sounds are more attractive than regular sounds, presumably because they resemble the sounds made by a sick or wounded fish struggling through the water.

It is often assumed that sharks are stupid because of their small brain size. However, Dr. Myrberg and his associates have found that sharks do learn from experience, that they learn rapidly, and that they retain this learning. This indicates a certain degree of intelligence that is quite apropos for such a highly successful group of animals.

Dr. Myrberg's studies of open-sea sharks, funded by the Office of Naval Research, have been curtailed for budgetary reasons. His next project is an investigation of the social behavior of the blacknose shark, a small, inshore species that frequents boat channels and the deeper flats in the Greater Miami area. Do these sharks possess a social organization? Do they have dominance hierarchies? Do they show territorial behavior? Do males and females react the same to a given stimulus? Are these sharks more active at certain times of the day or night? These are some of the questions that Dr. Myrberg will be considering over the next few years.

Chemical oceanography is one of the smaller departments at RSMAS, but it is by no means neglected. One of its special facilities is a tritium laboratory, which measures radiocarbon and tritium in the ocean. It is estimated that before the atomic bomb there was only about one kilogram (2.2 pounds) of tritium in the entire world. Of this amount, constantly decaying and being renewed by natural forces, only a few grams existed in the air. The rest was in the water. Atomic bomb tests upset the tritium balance by adding about 300 kilos to the world supply and blasting most of it up into the high stratosphere. And so, to obtain data on how long tritium remains in the stratosphere, specially designed airplanes climb to 60,000 feet and suck in samples of the thin upper air. The "residence time" of tritium-bearing water vapor is also an indicator of how long normal water vapor remains in the stratosphere. Samples of tritium-bearing water collected in the ocean have been analyzed for GEOSECS, and RSMAS also does its own investigations of ocean currents using tritium as the tracer. (Any ocean water now containing tritium must have been at the ocean surface at some point since 1958.)

The high-pressure lab is the domain of Dr. Frank Millero. A physical chemist, Dr. Millero studies the energy changes that are involved in a chemical reaction and looks for the mechanisms by which chemical reactions take place. The high-pressure equipment enables him to duplicate the conditions under which the chemical reactions of the ocean depths occur.

Dr. Millero looks at the world on a molecular level, in terms of chemical bonds, electron capture, and the like. When he considers the ocean, he wants to know how the physical properties of seawater are related to its composition, such as its density, its conductivity, and how well it transmits sound. He also wants to know what reactions take place among all the different substances dissolved in seawater and why they take place.

His quest has led him down an arduous trail of identifying and measuring all the chemical properties of the constituents of seawater, some of them quite complex compounds, and some present in only the minutest of trace quantities.

The work of a physical ocean chemist often raises new questions. For example, chemists like Dr. Millero know that finding *X* parts per million of copper in a seawater sample doesn't mean very much. A good deal of that copper is tied up in complex compounds with other elements and does not take part in the body chemistry of living organisms. Neither is it available for geological reactions. What counts is the amount of copper that is not tied up in this way, and Dr. Millero and his peers are working on techniques that will enable them to calculate such amounts for all the elements. Dr. Millero hopes also to develop a general mathematical model for the chemical processes of the ocean, and to relate these processes to the chemistry of human body fluids.

Originally RSMAS had separate departments of physical oceanography and atmospheric science. In 1977 they were merged to form the division of meteorology and physical oceanography. The physical oceanographers have concentrated on mapping detailed profiles of currents, from the coast of Oregon to the equatorial Atlantic. Working with the chemical oceanography department, they also study large-scale transport and mixing of water masses.

The physical oceanography programs at RSMAS are largely field-oriented, with the aim of gathering data to refine existing theories or develop new ones. The largest project in which RSMAS' department has been involved was GATE, the acronym for GARP Atlantic Tropical Experiment. (As one oceanographer wryly pointed out, this makes GATE a second-generation acronym.) The objective of GATE was to learn more about the processes that govern tropical weather, with the long-range goal of improving weather forecasting and perhaps even predicting long-term climatic fluctuations. The project involved the gathering of vast quantities of simultaneous observations from Latin America to Africa, and from the top of the atmosphere to a mile beneath the ocean surface.

GATE was a huge project, involving many government agencies as well as universities. Research vessels were lent by France, West Germany, Russia, and East Germany as well as by the United States. Scientists from seventy nations took part. Forty ships, a dozen specially equipped aircraft, satellites, and data buoys contributed information that was subsequently worked up into mathematical models for computerized weather forecasting.

The Rosenstiel School was the major nongovernmental American participant in GATE. Working in the area between the eastern tip of Brazil and the bulge of West Africa, the RSMAS scientists did extensive current profiling and gathered masses of data on the effect of the region's variable winds on the speed, volume, and makeup of the currents. A major subject of investigation was the Equatorial Undercurrent, an intense, east-flowing ribbon of water found at depths of 160 to 500 feet. For the first time, it was learned that the Equatorial Undercurrent meanders both north and south of the equator with a slow, wavelike motion.

The Department of Marine Geology and Geophysics has three major research programs: the dynamics of continental-shelf sedimentation; paleoclimatology; and the genesis and recycling of the oceanic crust. When one of the scientists began developing a model of the shelf sedimentation process, he found it was so complicated that he had to work up four submodels, one for each method by which material arrives on the shelf. One is the "bed-load," heavy sediments that are carried down by rivers and dumped when they reach the ocean. Finer particles are suspended in the water for a time before settling out; still finer particles float for even longer before coming to rest on the bottom. Normally, the biggest, heaviest particles settle closest to the land, finer ones progressively farther out. But currents pick them up and redistribute them. A great deal of material comes as dust particles from the air. Then there are dissolved minerals carried down by rivers or in from the open sea; these may undergo chemical reactions that bind them into insoluble compounds which settle down like the precipitate in a test tube, or they may be taken up by living organisms and sink to the bottom when those organisms die. In fact, so much of the shelf sediments are the remains of once-living organisms that ecology must be brought in for a complete study.

Sediment studies are also the key to the paleoclimatologists' success as they link the microscopic fossil shells of such organisms as forams and radiolarians to long-past climatic patterns. Largely on the basis of these studies, a team headed by Dr. Cesare Emiliani contributed to the development of the standard paleoclimatic maps. Dr. Emiliani is also attempting to correlate the Great Flood of the Bible and other flood legends of ancient civilizations with the rise in sea level produced by the melting of the last great ice sheets from 14,000 to 9,000 years ago. Although this so far is speculation, his documentary evidence indicates that most of the water from the melting of the North American ice sheet poured down the Mississippi River to the Gulf of Mexico. Dr. Emiliani theorizes that the rate of melting of the North American ice sheet was so fast that a perceptible rise in sea level occurred in as little as a year, with the result that many centers of culture that had grown up near sea level were drowned.

The scientists studying the oceanic crust hope to find the answers to the question "What causes seafloor spreading?" Their approach is to study the petrological, geochemical, and physical properties of the crustal rocks and work backward from there. A practical aspect of the work is that it may lead to locating undersea ore deposits. The investigators have concentrated on two areas of the Mid-Atlantic Ridge. Another team has been gathering data on potential drilling sites for the IPOD (International Program of Ocean Drilling) project.

The RSMAS library, though not the largest in the country, is nevertheless of impressive size, with 22,000 books and subscriptions to 583 periodicals. Alan Baldridge, the English-born librarian, told me some of the problems of running a library for an oceanographic institution. Since RSMAS is a graduate school and research institution, there is very little material on an undergraduate or popular level. And, because scientists want to keep up with what their colleagues are doing, the emphasis is on periodicals rather than books. It takes seven or eight years for a scientist's work to get into a professional-level book, but only about two years to appear in a scientific journal.

Newly received periodicals go into a special "new today" rack for twenty-four hours, then to a "new this week" rack. This is an important convenience for scientists and students who want to keep up. Many of the periodicals are in foreign languages: Russian, German, and Japanese; and because of RSMAS' links with Latin America, in Spanish and Portuguese as well. This poses some problems because working scientists do not want to take time out to learn another language, and translators are not always easy to find. So far the school has been able to get graduate students in the foreign-language programs of the University of Miami to do the translating.

Everything in the library is accessible. Even reference books can be borrowed by special request. There is also an active interlibrary loan program. As Alan explained, libraries no longer try to be self-sufficient, even in such a specialized field as marine science. More and more they tend to depend on each other. RSMAS' principal trading partners are the nearby NOAA facility, the main campus of the University of Miami at Coral Gables, and the university's medical school, but it also cooperates with university and public libraries throughout the state. Thus, through the interlibrary loan system, the general public can borrow RSMAS' specialized books and periodicals.

RSMAS today has a faculty of about 80 and about 140 graduate students. The school can afford to be very selective in choosing its students; there are about 400 applications every year, of which about 20 are accepted for the graduate programs. In 1977 RSMAS added an undergraduate program in marine science. Undergrads have the option of taking a double major in marine science and biology, geology, physics, or chemistry. A BA program in marine science was also instituted for students who want a career in government, law, or business and need a background in marine affairs.

The graduate academic program is designed as an apprenticeship. Each student works closely with one scientist, and this experience is considered by the school as the most important part of his education. If the student and his mentor do not get along, a change can always be made. From what I saw, though, the relationship between students and professors at RSMAS was one of closeness and mutual respect.

A relatively new development at RSMAS is the postdoctoral fellowship, in which recent Ph.D. graduates spend a year or so in intensive research in an area of their own choosing. This serves a dual purpose. It is not only an excellent way to try out prospective faculty members; it also brings in new ideas. And without fresh ideas from outside even the finest research institution tends to go stale.

Let us return now to the other institutions on Virginia Key. The International Oceanographic Foundation was established in 1953 by the redoubtable F. G. Walton Smith with the aim of raising the public's level of knowledge about the ocean. Dr. Smith was originally a marine biologist, but his interests widened with the years, until they now encompass every aspect of the oceans. He considers oceanography the study of the oceans as a very complex energy system. The energy in this system may take different paths, such as the formation of waves and currents, the growth of living organisms, and chemical reactions in the water. This idea guided him in designing Planet Ocean, the IOF's educational exhibit on Virginia Key. Opened in 1975, the large exhibition hall features films and dioramas about the sea and man's use of it, a full-scale model of the submersible *Alvin,* and an excellent exhibit on the properties of water. There are also working models of an offshore oil-drilling rig, a tidal-power plant, and other marvels of ocean engineering.

The upper floor of the building houses the offices of the IOF and its two publications, the nationally circulated magazines *Sea*

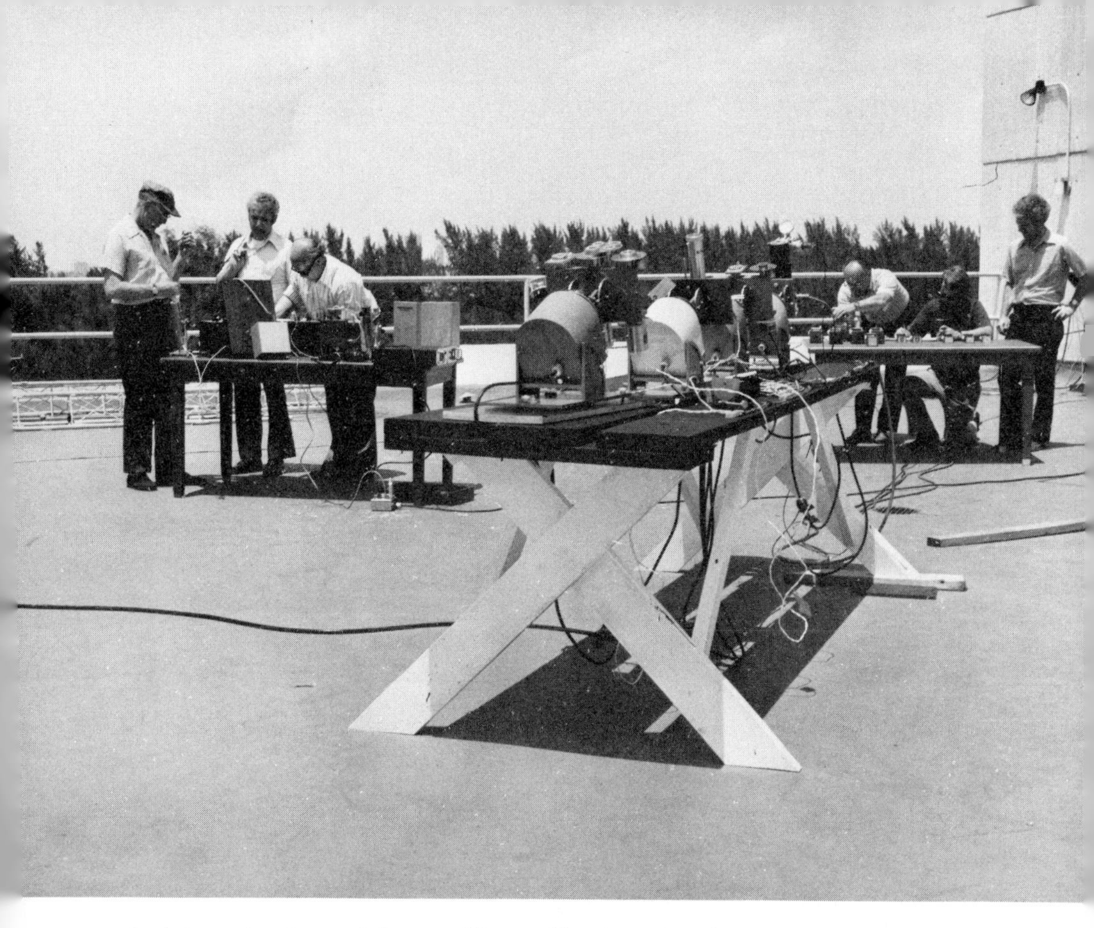

An international comparison and intercalibration of equipment for measuring incoming solar radiation was carried out at NOAA's Atlantic Oceanographic and Meteorological Laboratories in Miami, Florida. Six nations—Canada, France, Germany, Mexico, the U.S.A., and the U.S.S.R.—had their instruments coordinated. *Atlantic Oceanographic and Meteorological Laboratories*

Frontiers and *Sea Secrets*. Written on a popular level, these publications present marine subjects on a bimonthly schedule. *Sea Secrets* is devoted to answering readers' questions; the answers are researched and written by graduate students at RSMAS. *Sea Frontiers* features articles on topics of current interest, many of them written by RSMAS scientists. Nothing gets into type without having first been checked by Dr. Smith.

On the plot of land next to the IOF rises the huge, modernistic building of NOAA's Atlantic Oceanographic and Meteorological Laboratory. Opened in 1973, the AOML employs about 150 people in its four component laboratories of physical oceanography, ocean chemistry, marine geology and geophysics, and sea-air interaction. There is no marine-biology program, as this is handled by the neighboring NOAA Southeast Fisheries Center.

Briefly, the physical-oceanography lab concentrates on studies of such major ocean phenomena as the Loop Current in the Gulf

Dr. Bonnie McGregor and George Merrill of the AOML ready a gravity corer for lowering from a NOAA research vessel.

Atlantic Oceanographic and Meteorological Laboratories

of Mexico and the causes of the meandering of the Gulf Stream. It also investigates the nature of tidal processes in the open ocean and on the continental shelf, using data from tide gauges mounted on the seafloor.

The ocean-chemistry laboratory, established in 1976, works chiefly on analyses of the constituents of coastal waters and bottom sediments, as in the huge MESA project investigating pollution in New York Bight, the area from New York to Delaware, extending to the edge of the continental shelf. It also conducts an active program with the National Park Service to identify agricultural pollutants, such as pesticide residues and fertilizers, that move through the Everglades into Florida Bay. The ocean-chemistry group also studies the chemical dynamics of the Gulf of Mexico-Caribbean system and the substances it contributes to the North Atlantic gyre system.

The marine geologists and geophysicists have two major programs of investigation. One is the processes that control sedimentation on the continental shelf. The other is the formation of metal-bearing deposits at the boundaries of the oceanic crustal plates.

The sea-air interaction group takes for its province the lower few hundred feet of the atmosphere and the upper few hundred feet of the ocean. Regarding the sea as the great reservoir of solar-heat energy that fuels the world's weather, they study the mechanisms and the physical principles that govern the exchange of heat and other forms of energy between sea and air. The long-term objectives are to improve predictions of storms, abnormally high storm surges, destructive waves, and similar marine phenomena, and to increase the understanding of the forces that shape long-term climatic trends.

For the last few years the AOML's major effort has been Project MESA (described in detail in Chapter 17). But it has also been a major contributor to GATE and MODE (Mid-Ocean Dynamics Experiment), and in 1978 it was scheduled to take part in POLYMODE, a joint United States-Soviet Union sequel to MODE. One part of POLYMODE will be a three-year study of thermal patterns in the North Atlantic, using data from NOAA satellites and from surface ships to trace and analyze the meanders of the Gulf Stream, the formation of eddies, and the formation and disintegration of water-mass fronts in the Sargasso Sea. The physical oceanographers will also chart currents in the North Pacific with drift buoys as a preliminary to another huge project called FGGE (First GARP Global Experiment).

The ocean-chemistry group, as a part of its work on MESA, developed a technique of chemical analysis that can distinguish sewage products from other organic matter in seafloor sediments, such as the remains of phytoplankton. It has also developed new methods of detecting pesticides and PCBs (polychlorinated biphenyls) in the water.

Scientists of the marine-geology and geophysics group have published studies on the instability of continental-shelf sediments that were of great interest to oil producers. In fact, the Shell Oil Company and scientists from Texas A & M later joined in the AOML studies. Another aspect of their work was investigating the role played by submarine canyons in moving sediments down off the continental shelf into the abyssal plains. Data so far seem to indicate that the canyons play a minor role.

The scientists who investigated metallogenesis found ribbons of high-manganese deposits stretching for miles on either side of certain metal-bearing hot springs on the Mid-Atlantic Ridge. The inference is that these manganese trails were produced as the crustal plates moved slowly away from their point of origin in the Mid-Atlantic Rift. These studies yield not only further confirmation of the seafloor-spreading theory but may also have a long-range practical application for seafloor mining.

The sea-air interaction group has made several flights through hurricanes to gather data such as radar pictures and laser profiles of storm waves. Less dramatically, it has used remote sensors to track dumped sewage acoustically, making use of the slight difference in density of the sewage-clouded currents and the clearer surrounding water. The results were confirmed with chemical tests and found accurate. The sea-air group has also used satellites, ships, and aircraft to gather data on internal waves on the continental shelf. A result was the discovery that in New York Bight internal waves are apparently responsible for churning up clouds of sediment that rise as much as 23 feet (7 meters) above the bottom. One of their tentative conclusions is that internal waves play an important part in transporting ocean sediments and in bringing nutrients up from the deep to the sunlit upper layers where they nourish plankton. One of the most helpful tools the AOML scientists have is a computer called LIAR, which extracts and interprets information from photos, graphic images, and taped signals. (LIAR does not describe the machine's truthfulness—it stands for Laboratory for Image Analysis and Research.)

Also in the works is a joint United States-Soviet Union atlas of the central North Atlantic ocean basins and continental margins. Plans called for this major work to be published in 1977.

A great deal is going on at Virginia Key, and the master plan calls for even more. Miami-Dade Community College plans to build a school for training marine technicians. It is expected that other schools, government agencies, and industries will set up their own research institutions there. If things develop according to plan, the Rosenstiel School and the NOAA labs will be the core of the world's largest center of tropical marine research.

15

Scripps Institution of Oceanography

BIGGEST OF THE GIANTS

The leading oceanographic institution in the United States—perhaps in the world—is Scripps Institution of Oceanography. Located on the edge of the wealthy California residential town of La Jolla, Scripps spreads its complex of World War I-vintage and ultramodern buildings along the edge of the blue Pacific. Today it is a part of the University of California, San Diego, and a bastion of the United States oceanographic establishment. But it was not always so. In the beginning, Scripps was a small, unaffiliated experimental institute and nearly starved to death for lack of backing.

Scripps had its genesis romantically enough in the summer of 1891, when a young college instructor, William Ritter, took his newlywed bride on a honeymoon trip to the southern California shore at San Diego. Ritter was then a zoology instructor at the University of California in Berkeley, and passionately devoted to his specialty. In fact, he and his wife spent part of their honeymoon wading around the rocks searching for a rare blind fish on which he was writing his doctoral dissertation for Harvard.

While Ritter had been slogging through his graduate work at Harvard, the Marine Biological Laboratory was being set up at Woods Hole, and this fired him with the ambition of creating a

West Coast counterpart to that august New England institution. In the summer of 1892, he took a few students and a large tent and set up his first marine laboratory at Pacific Grove, not far south of San Francisco. For a decade Ritter and his students between them explored the Pacific coast from the Mexican border to Alaska. But problems remained to be solved before Ritter's dream became a reality.

One was the choice of a suitable location. Ritter found the area between Los Angeles and San Diego ideal from the standpoint of variety and abundance of marine life. But he also needed land at an affordable price and a guaranteed supply of uncontaminated seawater. Southern California at that time was going through one of its periodic land booms, and developers were creating new communities along the coast almost overnight. These new communities, as was the custom, used the sea as a receptable for their raw sewage. This was convenient and cheap for the developers, but fatal for marine-oriented scientific work.

The other big problem was lack of funds. The University of California did not want to spend the money to acquire the large shoreline tract that was needed to preserve a natural environment for research. And Ritter, on a professor's pay, could certainly not afford it on his own. At length, in 1903, Ritter was introduced to a wealthy newspaper publisher, E. W. Scripps, who lived near San Diego. Scripps and his sister, Miss Ellen B. Scripps, together with a number of other prominent San Diegans, established a Marine Biological Association and began raising funds. In 1907 the association purchased 170 acres of barren desert scrub and rocky hills fourteen miles north of the little city of San Diego. Ritter stepped down from his post as chairman of the zoology department at the University of California to become scientific director of the association, though he continued as a professor at the university.

Since Mr. Scripps, an Illinois farm boy who had made good, did not think much of the business ability of scientists, he installed a local grain merchant as head of the board of trustees. However, Scripps, like the rest of Ritter's backers, believed firmly that Ritter's biological station would bring distinction to San Diego and increase the value of their real-estate holdings in the area.

The hardheaded Scripps was philanthropic as well as rich. So was his tough-minded, independent sister, eighteen years older than he, who had defied convention to read proof, write, and keep the books for the first family newspaper. Her native business ability eventually gained her a sizable fortune of her own.

The Scrippses were anxious to see their infant institution produce results. Scripps frequently dropped in at the lab to chat with the director and tell him how he would like to have things run—a time-consuming interruption for the scientist. But it was hard to argue with a man who was responsible for your lab's existence and who was generous enough to lend you his yacht, equipping it with all the paraphernalia needed by a research vessel. When the yacht ran on a reef and was wrecked after a mere season or two, Scripps held his temper in check and growled, "Well, at least that ought to kill those damned fleas on her!" Ellen, her enthusiasm undiminished, supplied funds for building a new research vessel. By their generosity with funds and their shrewd advice, the brother and sister earned the honor of having the institution named for them.

The first building, a wooden sleep-in lab, went up near the present site of the institution in 1905. It was followed by several bungalows for the scientific staff. Scripps, with visions of founding an intellectual colony of rather ascetic nature, offered a free lot to any of the scientists who would agree to build a house worth not more than $2,500. Even in those preinflation days, that meant rather spartan accommodations, and the site lay at the end of a steep dirt road, far from both lab and town. Only two men accepted the deal. But life was rather spartan anyway in the early days at the Scripps Institution. Summers were hot, dry, and dusty. Many of the ornamental shrubs and trees that Scripps had donated to brighten things up died in dry spells. Winters were chilly and rainy, and the unpaved access roads often became impassable strips of mud. Things improved gradually, however.

In 1912 the State of California finally accepted the institution into the state university system as the Scripps Institution for Biological Research. Originally the state had turned down Ritter's approaches, not wishing to spend taxpayers' money on what looked like a white elephant, but by 1912 Ritter and his scientific team had demonstrated its worth. In 1915 the famous Scripps Pier was built, jutting a thousand feet out into the ocean, a gift of Ellen. More scientists were hired, at a salary of $100 a month. One of Ritter's associates made a sabbatical visit to marine institutions in Britain, Germany, Italy, and Norway, bringing back the latest ideas in research and technology.

These international contacts may have been suspect in the eyes of the neighbors—even then southern California may have had its quota of paranoids—for during World War I Ritter's assistant came under suspicion as a German agent, simply because he spoke German. Soon afterward, local vigilantes decided that the night watchman, as he patrolled the pier, was secretly signaling to German submarines with his lantern!

The institution survived the incident, however, and by the time Ritter retired in 1923 it had already begun to broaden its investigations into marine physics and chemistry, using the pier as a platform for studying waves, tides, and other physical oceanographic phenomena and for taking water samples. Ritter's successor, a dynamic Texan geologist named T. Wayland Vaughan, added marine geology to the Scripps Institution's spectrum of activities. By 1926, when E. W. Scripps died, the institution deserved its new title of Scripps Institution of Oceanography.

In 1936 a Norwegian meteorologist-oceanographer, Harald Sverdrup, succeeded Vaughan as director of Scripps. With a background in Arctic meteorology, ocean currents and tides, and air-sea interactions, he was a veteran of the seven-year Arctic expedition organized by Roald Amundsen, and he had accompanied the British explorer Sir Hubert Wilkins on his abortive attempt to reach the North Pole by submarine in 1931. Sverdrup was the first blue-water oceanographer to head Scripps, and by the time he left in 1948 the institution was firmly committed to deep-water research.

Today Scripps has a fleet of five research ships. There is also an unusual floating instrument platform acronymically titled FLIP and a bargelike oceanographic research buoy called ORB. The

The Scripps-designed Deep Tow vehicle, fitted with complex electronic equipment, allows oceanographers to map the fine geological structure of the sea bottom. Beneath the Deep Tow's body is a remote-controlled net for capturing plankton near the seafloor.

Scripps Institution of Oceanography

institution has grown to 64 buildings on 230 acres, the staff numbers about 1,200, and there are 185 graduate students, who rank as staff members. At any one time, over 200 research projects may be in progress. It costs approximately $37 million a year to operate Scripps.

Sharing the Scripps campus are the headquarters of the University of California's Institute of Marine Resources, a branch of the University's Institute of Geophysics and Planetary Physics, and the Southwest Fishery Center of NOAA. Sprawled across the tops of the bluffs above Scripps is the campus of UCSD (University of California, San Diego).

The research fleet is based at Point Loma, fifteen miles from the campus, near several Navy research stations. One of these is the Naval Ocean Systems Center, where dolphins and sea lions are trained to assist divers. The Scripps Pier juts out into the San Diego-La Jolla Underwater Park, part of which is an ecological reserve.

It is expected that students will continue all the way to the Ph.D. Average time to complete the requirements is five years. Degrees are granted by UCSD, of which Scripps became part in 1961. Previously they had been granted by Berkeley or by UCLA.

Some idea of the variety of research done at Scripps may be gathered from a sampling of the titles of papers published in a recent year:

"Antibiotics from marine organisms in the Gulf of California."
"Implications of heat flow for metallogenesis in the Bauer Deep."
"Coccoliths as paleosalinity indicators."
"Torsional overtone dispersion from correlations of *S* waves to *SS* waves."
"Occurrence of lead in tuna."
"Acanthaster: tests of the time course of coral destruction."
"Internal-wave breaking and microstructure."
"Microbial geochemistry of oxygen."
"Recovery of equipment from the ocean floor."
"Regional aspects of deep-sea drilling in the Indian Ocean."
"The ocean as a power source."
"Observations on the anatomy of the respiratory systems of the river otter, sea otter, and harp seal."

Some of the research appears to have no connection at all with oceanography: neuromuscular responses of sloths; isolation and properties of the envelope of spinach chloroplasts; feather carotenoids of an interspecific hybrid flamingo. But these are either applications of marine research work done at Scripps or contribute to the understanding of the physiological processes that keep sea life going.

Some of the major ongoing investigations involve studies of air-sea interactions in the North Pacific, with potential applications in weather forecasting; the role of silicon in biological systems and its possible implication in cancer and other diseases; earthquake prediction; and the formation of manganese nodules on the deep-sea floor. Another aspect of the manganese-nodule study is the possible ecological consequences of large-scale nodule mining—large-scale mining is the only kind that would pay off.

The largest single project is the DSDP, or Deep-Sea Drilling Project, which is paid for by the NSF and managed by Scripps. Eight American institutions share the work of DSDP; West Germany, France, Britain, Japan, and the Soviet Union contribute funds and scientists to this truly international project.

The DSDP is probably man's most ambitious geological exploration to date. It involves the near-impossible feat of managing a string of drill pipe anywhere from two to four miles long, from the unstable, unanchored platform of a ship on the ever-moving surface of the ocean. No ordinary vessel would do for this demanding task. Scripps chartered the specially equipped *Glomar Challenger*. It is only because of the technological breakthroughs achieved since the mid-1960's that deep-ocean drilling has become possible at all. One was dynamic positioning, a system of holding the drill ship virtually motionless in position over the hole. It is accomplished with a sonar beacon on the seafloor beside the hole, which beams signals to receivers on the ship. The sonar receivers are linked to computers that control the ship's four thrusters. Whenever the ship drifts out of position, the thrusters deliver the correct combination of forces to bring it back on site. So sensitive and responsive is the system that it keeps the ship within a radius of a hundred feet from the hole. Compared to the length of the drill string, this amount of motion is insignificant, and the flexible drill string absorbs it easily.

The other great breakthrough, called reentry, makes it possible to pull up a drill string, change the dulled bit, and send it back down the hole again to drill deeper. An important part of the system is a large funnel, sixteen feet across, over the drill hole, which guides the drill assembly back into position. The truly amazing part, however, is the way in which the drill operator can find the funnel, hidden beneath thousands of feet of water. The tip of the drill string is fitted with a small sonar scanner that emits a stream of pings. These signals are echoed back to the scanner by

DYNAMIC POSITIONING AND RE-ENTRY

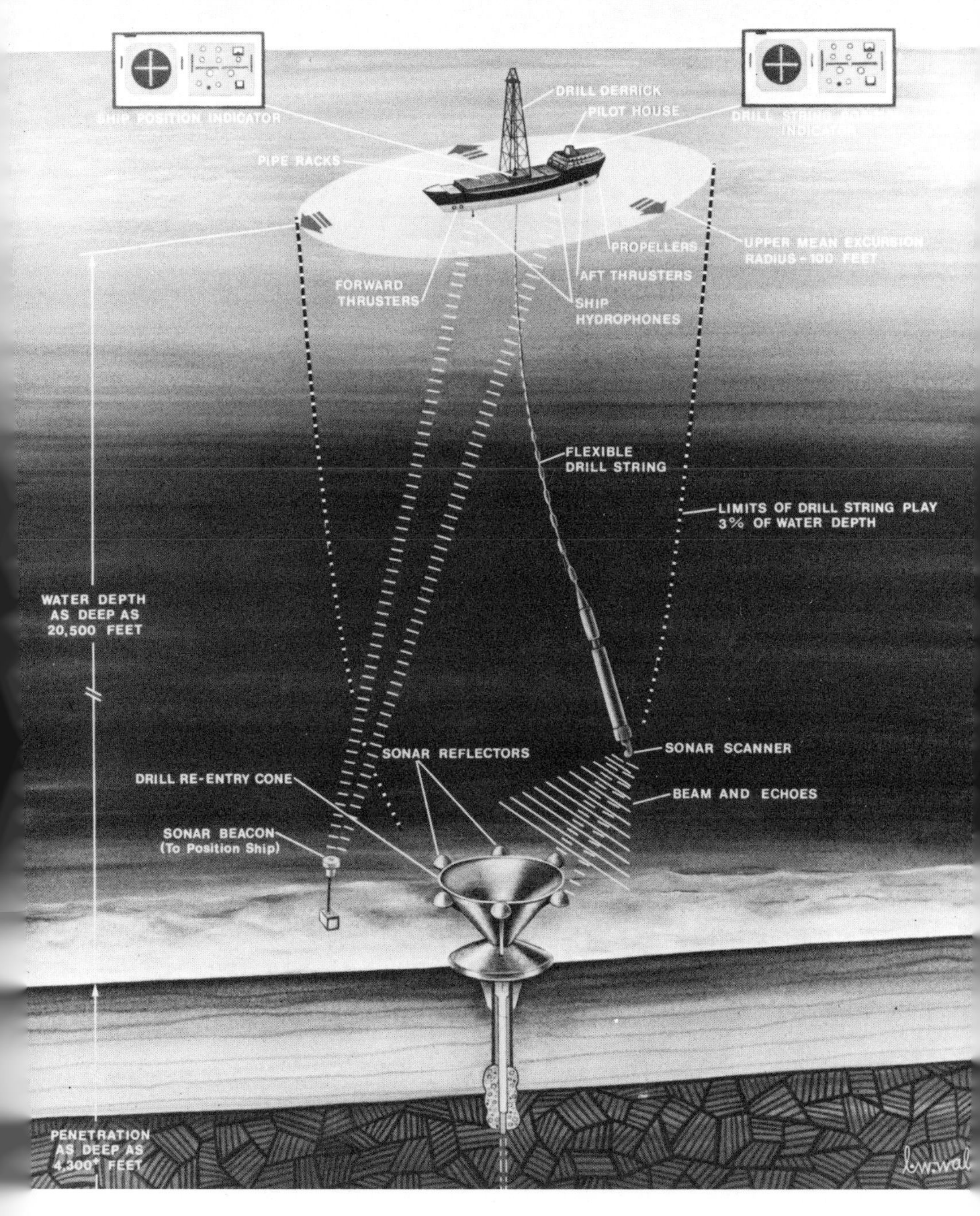

An artist's concept of the *Glomar Challenger*'s dynamic positioning and re-entry systems.

Deep Sea Drilling Project, Scripps Institution of Oceanography

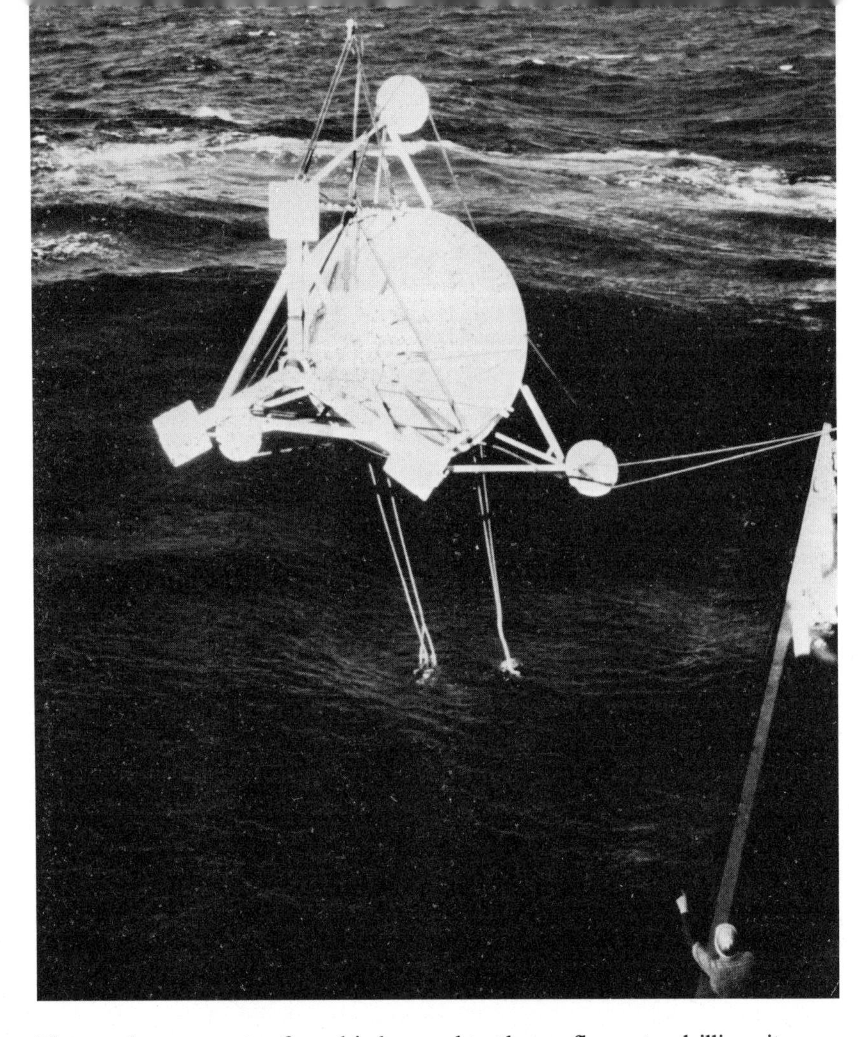

The ponderous reentry funnel is lowered to the seafloor at a drilling site.
Deep Sea Drilling Project, Scripps Institution of Oceanography

three sonar reflectors spaced around the rim of the funnel, so that the operator can tell where the drill bit is in relation to the funnel. With this guidance, he controls a water-jet device on the drill string that moves it into position for reentry. The first successful reentry was achieved on Christmas Day, 1970, while the *Glomar Challenger* was drilling in the Caribbean.

The reentry system makes it possible to obtain rock cores from very deep strata, which give geologists evidence about the early history of the seafloor that they had never obtained before. Previously, drilling had to be stopped when the bit wore out, because there was no way to get it back into the hole. However, it is not necessary to pull up the whole drill string each time you want a core. An ingenious modification—a detachable core barrel inside the drill pipe—enables cores to be pulled up at any time without interrupting drilling.

Crewmen check a massive rotary drill bit at sea on the *Glomar Challenger*.
Deep Sea Drilling Project, Scripps Institution of Oceanography

Map shows the forty-four legs of the Deep Sea Drilling Project, which took valuable core samples from the floor of every ocean but the Arctic. The five-year voyage began and ended at Norfolk, Virginia.
Scripps Institution of Oceanography

Since the *Glomar Challenger* began its epic series of voyages in August 1968, it has traveled over 240,000 nautical miles, drilled more than 600 holes, and recovered more than 26 miles of cores. It has drilled in the Atlantic, Pacific, and Indian Oceans, and in the Caribbean and Mediterranean Seas. The deepest it penetrated into the earth's crust beneath the ocean floor was 5,709 feet, in the Atlantic. The deepest water in which it drilled was at Site 212 on Leg 22 in the Indian Ocean: 20,483 feet. The drill string used on this site reached 22,192 feet down from the surface of the water.

What is the purpose of all this activity? To increase man's knowledge of the history of the Earth. Geologists had long been able to study the continents. But 71 percent of the Earth's surface is blanketed by water, with an average depth of about 12,000 feet. Even with dredges and piston corers, scientists had no way of reaching more than a short distance beneath the surface of the ocean floor, so that they could sample only the most recently formed rocks and sediments. As a result, most of the history of the oceans was a mystery. Theories flourished, but facts were scanty—until the DSDP provided masses of new data.

Here are some of the DSDP's scientific achievements: DSDP cores provided confirmation for the theory of seafloor spreading and continental drift. It was also found that the ocean basins are young, geologically speaking. The oldest rock recovered from beneath the seafloor has been dated at 160 million years; the oldest known continental rock is 3.6 billion years. Analysis of the cores revealed some surprising developments: Once, about 12,000 million years ago, the Mediterranean dried up entirely. The Atlantic began as a rift valley filled with fresh water, then became a dead sea of very salty, stagnant water before widening into its present form. Some deep ocean basins were once dry land, as fossils in the cores indicate. Antarctica has been covered with ice for at least 20 million years—three to four times the length of time geologists had previously believed. In addition, the *Glomar Challenger* struck oil under 12,000 feet of water in the Gulf of Mexico, in a type of formation that was previously known to occur only in shallow water. This discovery has raised new questions about the origin of the Gulf of Mexico.

There are also long-term benefits from the work of the DSDP. Economically, it has increased our knowledge of what kinds of mineral deposits we can expect to find beneath the sea, and in what kinds of locations we can expect to find them. The technological discoveries of dynamic positioning and reentry are already in use by commercial oil producers. On the environmental front, the DSDP cores are enabling chemical oceanographers to develop mathematical models of the way the ocean will respond to changes in river runoff, the inflow of manmade chemicals, and changes in climate.

Less awesome in scope, but also useful, is the tethered-float breakwater system based on a concept of Professor John Isaacs, one of Scripps's grand old men. Born into a wealthy and distinguished family, Isaacs dropped out of college and became a commercial fisherman, later returning to get a degree in engineering. A member of the team that carried out the scientific studies of the first atomic tests on Bikini Atoll, he is a storehouse of fantastic ideas. One is to use nuclear power to blast artificial harbors in areas where rivers and currents do not bring sediment to choke the harbor up. Another is to tow giant icebergs from the Antarctic to water-starved coastal cities like Los Angeles. Incidentally, a French firm is currently making plans to tow Antarctic bergs to Saudi Arabia, wrapped in plastic foam to keep them from melting en route.

The tethered-float breakwater is one of Isaacs' simplest and most elegant ideas. Details of the system were worked out by Isaacs' young associate, Richard Seymour, a Scripps graduate. In essence, it consists of tying large, inflated plastic spheres to a chain of sunken barges. Linked in a pattern six spheres across and of indefinite length, the spheres absorb and reflect a large proportion of the energy contained in oncoming waves. Pilot tests with beachball-sized spheres have shown that the tethered breakwater can reduce the force of waves by 60 percent. Tests with full-sized spheres of five to ten feet diameter are expected to do even better, reducing fifty-foot waves to five feet. The potentialities are tre-

The tethered-float breakwater developed by Scripps' Dr. John Isaacs and Richard Seymour gets its first field test.

Scripps Institution of Oceanography

mendous: a relatively cheap, easily constructed, and highly effective wave barrier that can protect not only harbors but offshore oil-drilling platforms, or create harbors if need be. The tethered breakwater could be immensely useful in areas like the North Sea, where oil rigs are frequently endangered by storm waves up to fifty feet in height.

Another grand old man of Scripps is physiologist Per Scholander, now retired. Swedish-born and Norwegian-raised, Prof. Scholander studied medicine at the University of Oslo but never practiced it. Instead, his fascination with research led him first to a study of lichens in Greenland, then to other organisms that survive under extremely adverse conditions. He has studied the special mechanisms of breathing, blood circulation, and heartbeat in diving birds and mammals, including hippos and human divers. He has investigated the fish that live at the bottoms of certain deep fjords in Labrador, where the water temperature is always below the freezing point of fresh water. These fish possess none of the natural antifreezes that protect other fish which thrive at subfreezing temperatures. Their super-cooled body fluids will crystallize and freeze solid in seconds if brought to the surface and touched with a piece of ice. But in the deep water there is no ice to touch off crystallization, and so the fish survive. Scholander has also analyzed the ability of Australian aborigines to survive, naked, the subfreezing nights of their desert homeland. Another of his studies concerned the ability of mangrove trees to live in salt water, which kills all other trees. The answer turned out to be that

Dr. Per Scholander of SIO disregards the rising tide as he measures sap tension of mangroves in a Florida swamp to learn how mangroves can thrive in salt water, deadly to all other trees.

Scripps Institution of Oceanography

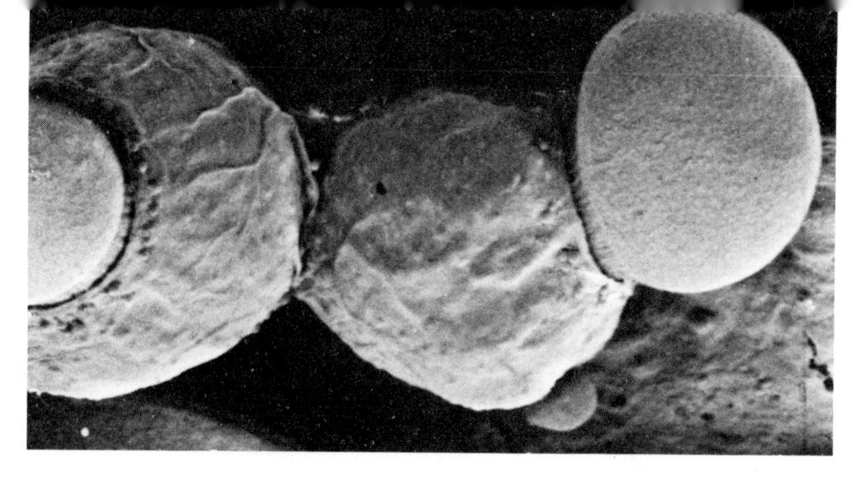

This scanning electron micrograph, taken by a Scripps researcher, shows eggs emerging from the reproductive organs of a Japanese feather star.
Dr. Nicholas D. Holland

the mangroves extract fresh water from salt water by reverse osmosis. One of the classic pictures in the Scripps archives is a photo of Scholander sitting beneath a big beach umbrella, clad only in shorts and sun helmet, his feet covered by the rising tide as he studies the sap tension in mangroves in a swamp near Miami, Florida.

Some of the investigations undertaken at Scripps in a typical year, 1975, are interesting, too. A marine-biology group studied

One of the world's oddest research vessels, Scripps' 355-foot FLIP, is shown here in its horizontal towing position and its vertical operating position. FLIP is an acronym for Floating Instrument Platform.
Scripps Institution of Oceanography

the breeding cycle of the Japanese feather star, a bottom-dwelling animal related distantly to true starfish and sea cucumbers. All through their range, Japanese feather stars spawn at exactly the same time: midafternoon on the first day of the first-quarter or last-quarter moon in the first two weeks of October. The Scripps biologists hoped to find the environmental factors that control this remarkable synchronization.

The scientists of Scripps' Marine Physical Laboratory continued their underwater acoustical studies with FLIP, the unique floating instrument platform. Shaped like a cross between a boat and a long steel pipe, FLIP is towed to its site. Then water is pumped into ballast compartments until the rear end sinks down and the craft, mostly submerged, floats in a vertical position with only 55 feet of the bow end remaining above water to serve as lab and living quarters. Since most of FLIP's 355-foot length is underwater, the odd craft is remarkably stable. Surface waves affect it hardly at all. And it is an ideally quiet listening post for underwater acoustic research.

Other experiments involved a remote-controlled underwater robot vehicle called RUM (Remote Underwater Manipulator), which, among other accomplishments, located an acoustic sensor device on the sea floor, brought it up for repair, and replaced it again at a depth of 1,600 feet.

In a joint investigation headed by Dr. Gerald L. Kooyman of Scripps and Dr. Kenneth Norris of University of California, Santa Cruz, researchers lassoed young gray whales and tested their respiratory functions with a flow meter placed on their blowholes. The young whales were also fitted with radio-transmitter harnesses that permitted the scientists to track them. (A quick-corroding magnesium bolt let the harness drop off in a few days.) Photographs taken of the whales swimming freely showed that they began to open their blowholes and breathe out before they had quite reached the surface, sending up a powerful spray of water. The scientists also believed that the whales were careless about closing their blowholes when they began a dive, so that some water leaked into the upper part of the respiratory passage. (An inner plug prevents the water from reaching the lungs.) This water, too, would come up as spray (it does in the case of bottlenose dolphins). So it would appear that the whale's spout is made of water after all.

In a related experiment, young sea lions were trained to follow a moving platform over their pool and breathe into a gas-collecting apparatus so that their exhaled breath could be measured and analyzed.

Perched on a moving platform, Dr. Gerald L. Kooyman of Scripps holds a nose cone for experimental sea lion Houdini. The animal is trained to breathe into the nose cone as he swims after the platform for measurements of air flow and volume. With Dr. Kooyman is his colleague Dr. John B. West.
University of California at San Diego

Scripps researchers ran some unexpected risks. A team doing geological studies on Lake Tanganyika, in the great East African rift valley, found themselves captured by the Zairean Navy and held overnight on suspicion of spying. Undeterred, two of the team went on to study a geothermal steam field in Kenya.

One of the most newsworthy events was the discovery by Dr. Jeffrey Bada, a young marine chemist at Scripps, of a new method of dating fossils. Known as amino-acid racemization, it depends on the fact that fossils contain measurable amounts of amino acids, the building blocks of proteins. When the organism dies, its amino acids do not break down. They last for many thousands of years. But they do change their structure. A living organism's amino acids have a left-handed structural configuration (briefly, this means that a beam of light passed through them is twisted to the left). After the organisms die, the amino acids change to a right-handed configuration. This change is termed racemization.

The ratio between left- and right-handed forms of the amino acids gives the age of the fossil. The actual process of calculating the fossil's age is somewhat more complex; among other things, the average temperature must be known, since temperature controls the rate of change.

Amino-acid racemization dating covers a much longer period than carbon-14 dating. Carbon-14's upper limit is about 40,000 years; racemization can date objects up to a million years. Another advantage of the racemization technique is that carbon-14 dating requires large amounts of material, as much as a pound of bone, while racemization dating needs only a tiny chip.

Bada caused a furor among anthropologists and archaeologists when he dated a human skull that had been found in 1929 in a cliff

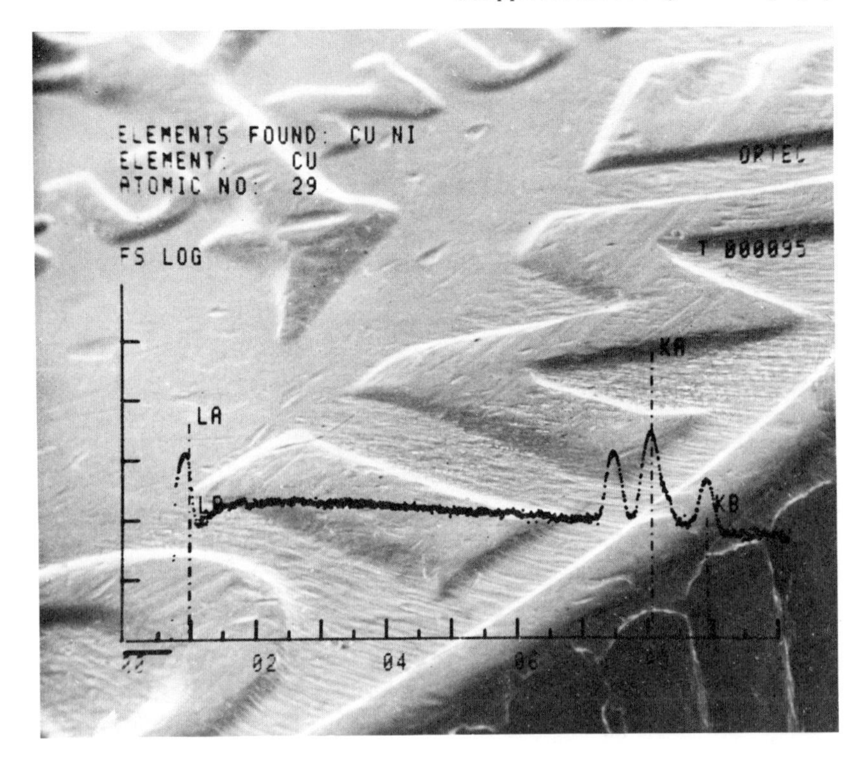

With one of Scripps' sophisticated scanning electron microscopes, scientists can observe and photograph a specimen while an X-ray attachment gives a simultaneous readout of its chemical analysis. The two results have been combined in this scanning electron micrograph of a dime. Note highly magnified fingerprint on edge of dime.

Scripps Institution of Oceanography

at Del Mar, near La Jolla, as at least 48,000 years old. The standard theory was that man had entered North America only 20,000 years ago at most. As a result of Bada's finding, some scholars are now claiming that man has been in North America as long as 100,000 years.

Bada's technique can also be applied to the teeth of living persons to verify their ages. This is already useful in longevity studies, since many of the people who claim great ages cannot back up their claims with birth certificates or any other records.

To help them in their labors, Scripps researchers and students can draw on a number of special facilities. One is the Analytical Facility, which boasts a scanning electron microscope with a magnification of 100,000 power, two electron microscopes for studying ultrafine structures, an X-ray diffractometer for studying crystal structures, atomic-absorption and X-ray spectrometers, an amino-acid analyzer, and a staggering array of other complex analytical devices. There is a cardiovascular research laboratory, an experimental aquarium, and a diving facility that trains UCSD members whose work takes them down under. People from Scripps and other departments of UCSD make about 4,000 dives a year. In fourteen years they racked up the enviable record of 60,000 accident-free dives.

There is also a hydraulics laboratory with a wind-wave channel, a wave and tidal basin, and another channel for studying the movement of sediments. Very sensitive low-level studies of natural and man-made radioactivity in the ocean are carried on in a separate lab off campus. Experiments with seals, whales, and large fish are conducted in the Physiological Research Laboratory Pool Facility, a 33-foot circular pool over which hangs a moving trolley that carries experimenters and instruments. An island in the middle of the pool holds small laboratories. When not on duty, the animals live in an adjoining holding pool.

The library contains nearly 112,000 bound volumes, 26,000 maps, 20,600 reprints, 27,000 documents, and outstanding collections in all aspects of oceanography and undersea technology. Special collections not in the library include the DSDP repository for cores from the Pacific and Indian oceans, a geological sample collection, a geologic data center, collections of marine vertebrates and invertebrates, and the oceanographic data archives.

Most of Scripps is not open to the public, but the outstanding Vaughan Aquarium-Museum is open free of charge every day. Over 400,000 visitors a year come to see the twenty-two marine-life tanks, featuring animals and plants grouped by habitat, and other attractions such as a thirty-pound mounted specimen of a coelacanth, the "living fossil" fish from the Indian Ocean, and

Scripps scientists obtained this rare photograph of colonial sea anemones fighting for territory on a rock in the intertidal zone. The anemones spar with special white-tipped tentacles used only in these conflicts.

Scripps Institution of Oceanography

exhibits on underwater photography, a wave tank, and displays explaining Scripps research projects. An unusual exhibit is a 10-by-18-foot artificial tide pool, featuring a two-hour tide cycle and actual waves, and, of course, living animals. The tide cycle and the waves can be adjusted for research purposes or to give visitors a chance to see what goes on.

The staff of the aquarium-museum, assisted by a corps of volunteer docents (lecturers), conducts educational programs and guides 61,000 students a year through the exhibits. Other programs include training for teachers, a Junior Oceanographers Corps, and a career-experience program for high-school and college students who are considering a career in marine biology or aquarium work. Research is done on problems of keeping the specimens alive and healthy, on coloration in fishes, and on fish diseases. In addition, the aquarium-museum's collectors provide several thousand specimens a year for Scripps scientists.

16

Some Other Leaders

One of the foremost marine-science research and teaching institutions is Texas A & M University. Far from being a provincial "cow college," Texas A & M is a huge and sophisticated university with many specialized divisions. A number of departments offer ocean-related programs—there are fourteen marine-related graduate degrees, granted by departments as varied as Business Administration and Agriculture—but most of the marine studies belong to the Department of Oceanography.

Established in 1949 to study the causes of oyster die-off along the Gulf Coast, the Department of Oceanography is now a part of the College of Geosciences at the main campus in College Station, about a hundred miles northwest of Houston. It is served by a shoreside laboratory complex on Pelican Island at Galveston. Also on Pelican Island is Moody College, a division founded in 1971, which offers undergraduate degrees in marine science, engineering, and transportation, and trains officers for the merchant marine.

Texas A & M, abbreviated as TAMU, is a small city in itself, with some 21,000 undergraduates and 4,500 graduate students. Its oceanography department is also one of the largest in the country, with about 120 graduate students at any one time. In its earlier

days Texas A & M turned out nearly one out of every four master's and doctor's degrees in oceanography granted in the United States, for it was one of the few institutions granting such degrees. As other schools began to produce oceanographers, Texas' percentage dropped, but it is still significant.

Special facilities include a trace-metal laboratory, petrographic and marine-soils labs, and the Galveston Coastal Zone Laboratory, which specializes in biological research. Oceanographic scientists and students also have free access to the university's nuclear, computer, and electron-microscope centers. The TAMU research fleet includes the 174-foot *Gyre*, a Navy-owned vessel built to Navy specifications, several smaller vessels for operations over the continental shelf, and a twenty-one-foot submersible, the *Diaphus*. The two-man submersible can explore the ocean at depths up to 1,200 feet and cruise at a speed of two knots (2 1/3 miles per hour). The *Gyre,* named for the ring-shaped circulatory systems that are one of Texas A & M's research specialties, has an 8,000-mile cruising range and carries nineteen scientists and eleven crew members. Such a high ratio of scientists to crew is unusual in a large research vessel.

Although the Department of Oceanography was established for coastal work in the Gulf of Mexico, its activities expanded year by year until they now spread as far afield as the Antarctic. From the original studies of the causes of oyster kills, its investigations have grown into every aspect of oceanography, and Texas A & M considers itself the Gulf Coast equivalent of Woods Hole and Scripps.

"Texas" and "oil" are practically synonymous in many minds, and a great deal of Texas A & M's research has to do with some aspect of petroleum or the petroleum industry. One program looks for the natural seabed seepages that release crude oil into the Gulf of Mexico and deposit as much as a ton of tar a year on its beaches. TAMU researchers locate the seeps by using low-frequency sound beams to home in on the bubbles of natural gas they give off. When they find a source of gas bubbles, they move in with underwater cameras to get a visual record. The submersible *Diaphus* has proved very useful in this work.

Another program analyzes the composition of the tar deposits on the beaches; so far, the results indicate that the tar has a uniform origin and may come from a single source. The chemists are also studying the processes by which tar forms and decomposes. In specially designed tanks, tar is artificially created by spreading oil on seawater and exposing it to air and sunlight. The oil is studied carefully as it spreads and ages. In addition to throwing new light on the question of what actually happens when

A student is helped into his diving suit for a course in underwater welding—part of the TAMU Sea Grant program.

Center for Marine Resources, Texas A & M University

Offshore drilling for oil is a major field of study for Texas A & M's Department of Oceanography.

Center for Marine Resources, Texas A & M University

oil is spilled at sea, these investigations may eventually help in locating new reserves of oil and natural gas on the ocean floor.

Much of the geological investigation is related to the oil industry. Determining how stable the bottom sediments are is important to prevent stationing offshore drilling rigs where a sudden slump, or sediment avalanche, may sweep them away. The formation of salt domes, the geological structures under which most petroleum is trapped, is another major field of research.

TAMU's geophysicists concentrate on sediments and crustal rocks of the Gulf and the Caribbean and also investigate the origin and nature of ocean basins. The meteorological oceanographers, a separate specialty at Texas A & M, also work primarily with the Gulf and Caribbean. The physical oceanographers' chief research programs involve ocean circulation, particularly the ring-shaped eddies that break off from the Gulf Stream and persist for months, and the effects on the Gulf Stream of topographical features of the seafloor, such as the New England Sea Mount chain.

In biological oceanography, programs of special interest include primary and secondary plankton productivity, bioacoustics, and toxicity of marine animals, such as paralytic shellfish poisoning. They also study coral-reef communities and other hard-bottom ecosystems in the Gulf, the effects of offshore oil drilling on marine life, and the bioenergetics of the Antarctic Ocean. Going a bit further afield, they draw on the talents of an anthropologist and a philosopher to investigate the possibilities of human communication with sea mammals.

Aquaculture is the province of the Department of Wildlife and Fisheries Sciences, in the College of Agriculture. Shrimp are the preeminent product of Texas A & M. Shrimp are a high-value crop, and TAMU's mariculturists have achieved yields of two tons an acre. They look forward to harvesting two and a half tons per acre several times a year as experience improves their technology. They have developed a three-level pond system in which baby shrimp begin in the highest and smallest pond and are moved downward to complete their growth in the largest pond. At one time the shrimp stopped growing; researchers found that the problem was caused by an infestation of the ponds with clams. As the clams secreted material for their shells, they removed calcium from the water, which then became too acid for the shrimp. Getting rid of the clams solved the problem.

An unusual shrimp-culture plant was set up in the high, arid plains of West Texas, utilizing natural underground supplies of salt water. Abandoned gravel pits were used for the first ponds, with mixed results. Later, specially designed ponds were dug, and the shrimp reached their market size of 5½ inches in a mere hundred days. Encouraged by the results, the experimenters added crabs and several species of fish to their stock. If successful, they will be able to put a previously worthless nature resource, the salt water, to productive use.

While the mariculture experts have been studying the commercial aspects of one species of invertebrate, another group has been busy sorting out and cataloging the university's extensive collection of scientific specimens. Almost 1,800 species of marine invertebrates, ranging from sea squirts to mollusks and crustaceans, have been cataloged, and work is proceeding on the fish and plankton collections.

The Pacific Northwest lies nearly 2,000 miles from the Gulf of Mexico and is completely different in nature. Instead of the gently sloping sandy plains and broad continental shelf of the Gulf Coast there are mountains, rocky coasts, and a narrow shelf that plunges swiftly into the ocean depths. In this region, known for its productive fisheries, are Oregon State University and the University of Washington.

Oregon State University is located in the pleasant small city of Corvallis in the fertile Willamette Valley, some fifty-six miles and one mountain range distant from the Pacific. The oceanographic course work is given at Corvallis, where most of the research facilities are located. The University's Marine Science Center at Newport, on Yaquina Bay, complements the Corvallis facilities.

Oceanography at OSU began in 1954 as a one-man effort when Dr. Wayne V. Burt joined the science faculty. A former high-school science teacher and Navy meteorologist, Dr. Burt had been sent to Scripps during World War II to learn the art of forecasting sea and swell conditions for the planned invasion of Japan. After the war he returned to Scripps to take graduate degrees in oceanography. Eventually an ONR grant of $10,000 sent him back to his home state of Oregon to start a program of oceanographic research.

At first the program consisted of Dr. Burt and a 16-foot run-about in which he explored the waters close to shore. His first office was a storage closet in the office of the dean of the School of Science. The next year brought modest improvements; he moved into a laboratory room belonging to the food technology division, sharing it with a Turkish graduate student (the Turk, having arrived on the scene first, got the desk by the window). Dr. Burt also began his open-sea operations as a passenger on the Coast Guard's monthly 25-mile run out from the coast off Newport.

Despite these unpromising beginnings, the oceanography program proved itself, the ONR increased its support, and a separate

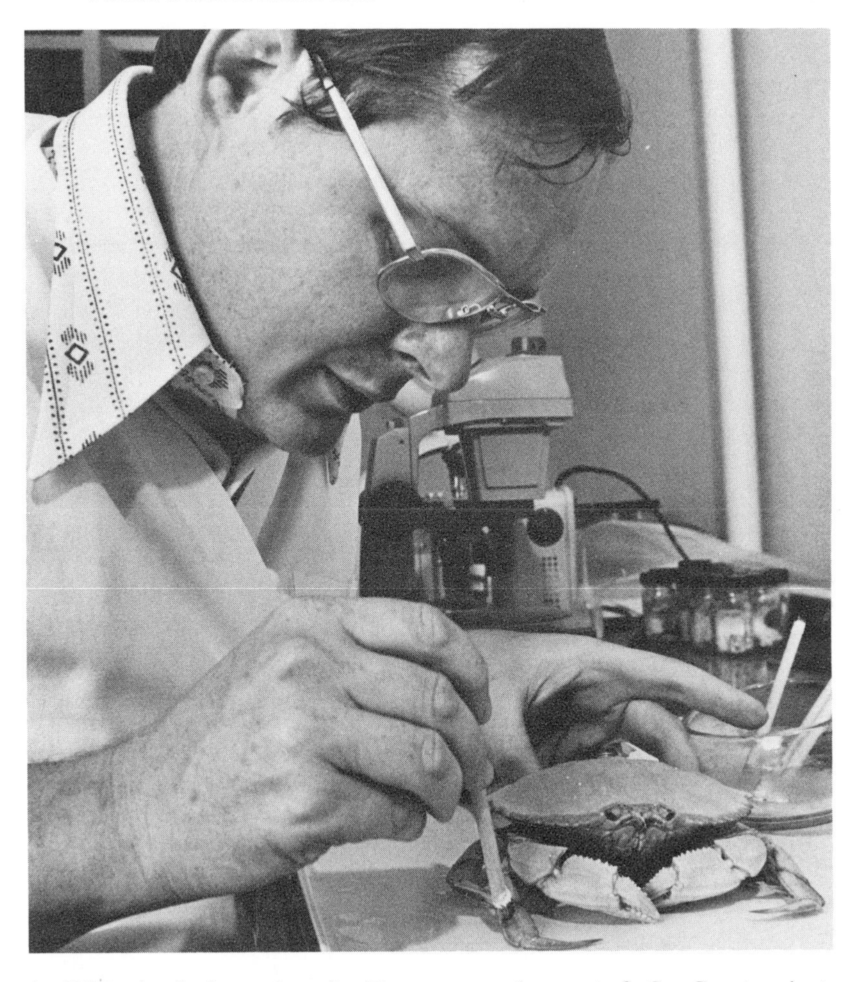

An OSU scientist freeze-brands a Dungeness crab as part of a Sea Grant project. The goal: to develop methods for permanently marking crustaceans for studies of growth rates and population dynamics.

Oregon State Sea Grant College Program

Department of Oceanography was established in 1959. From the very first, the training of oceanographers was considered equal in importance to research, and the school has been known for the close relationship between faculty and students.

In 1961 OSU acquired its first research vessel; until then the oceanographers had had to charter fishing boats or "piggyback" on Coast Guard vessels. In 1968 OSU received the nation's first Sea Grant award, helped by a sympathetic governor and state legislators, who secured the necessary matching funds. In 1971 OSU became one of the original four Sea Grant Colleges, and in 1972 the oceanography department was given the status of a full-fledged school of the university under the able leadership of Dean John V. Byrne, who had been with the department since 1960.

The portion of the Pacific off the Oregon coast had been a neglected region, oceanographically speaking. There was plenty for Dr. Burt and his colleagues and successors to investigate. One of their projects was to map the northward-flowing Davidson current, which appears only in winter. Another important program was a study of coastal upwelling. Upwelling is known for its role in bringing deep-water nutrients to the surface layers of the ocean and so increasing biological productivity. In the Pacific Northwest it is important for another reason—it often causes dense fogs that endanger shipping. OSU's investigators studied the relationship between winds and upwelling and developed a method for predicting upwelling on the basis of measurements of the wind's direction and strength.

The geological oceanographers have made many interesting discoveries, for instance, that the continental margin off Oregon is actually growing. Studies of fossil forams and radiolarians found in offshore rocks that are exposed at low tide showed that those rocks were originally formed at great depths. The inescapable conclusion is that the continental shelf is being uplifted in this region. The scientists believe that the continental shelf has increased five to ten miles in width over the last few million years because of this uplift. Another result of the geological oceanographers' investigations was the discovery of seabed placer deposits of magnetite ore, similar to those found on land in the northwest and sometimes mined for their gold and silver content.

Geophysics is a strong field at OSU, and this is reflected in the geophysical oceanography program. The School of Oceanography supports a seismograph station that is part of a worldwide network for monitoring earthquakes. Using seismic and gravity-measuring techniques, the geophysicists have found that the earth's crust is unusually thin just beyond the continental slope. By means of measuring magnetic variations, they have been able to trace the earthquake-prone San Andreas fault of California as it turns into a series of submerged, spreading ridges and fracture zones—part of the midocean ridge system—a hundred to three hundred miles off the coasts of Oregon and Washington.

In chemical oceanography, OSU members have found that measurements of the amounts of dissolved carbon dioxide and oxygen in the water are often better indicators of upwelling than the conventional measurements of temperature and salinity. And by measuring the distribution of chemicals in the water, they have found new information on the deep circulation of the North Pacific.

Biological oceanographers at OSU study a variety of organisms ranging from microscopic phytoplankton and bacteria to albacore (a member of the tuna family) and sea lions. Early research was focused on the poorly known deep-sea fauna off Oregon and on the dynamics of open-sea animals and phytoplankton in the coas-

These spidery-looking Farmer crabs are being studied by an OSU oceanographer to determine whether they have commercial potentialities.
Oregon State Sea Grant College Program

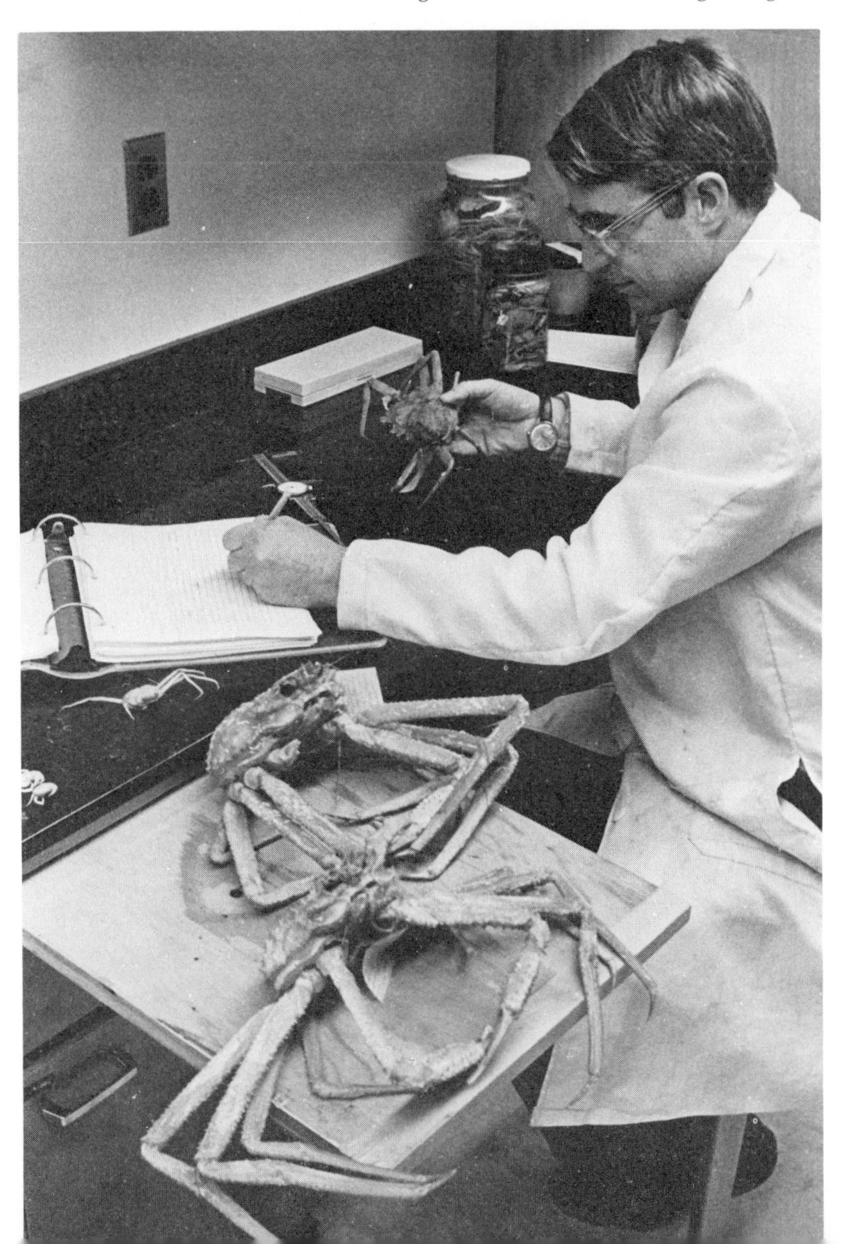

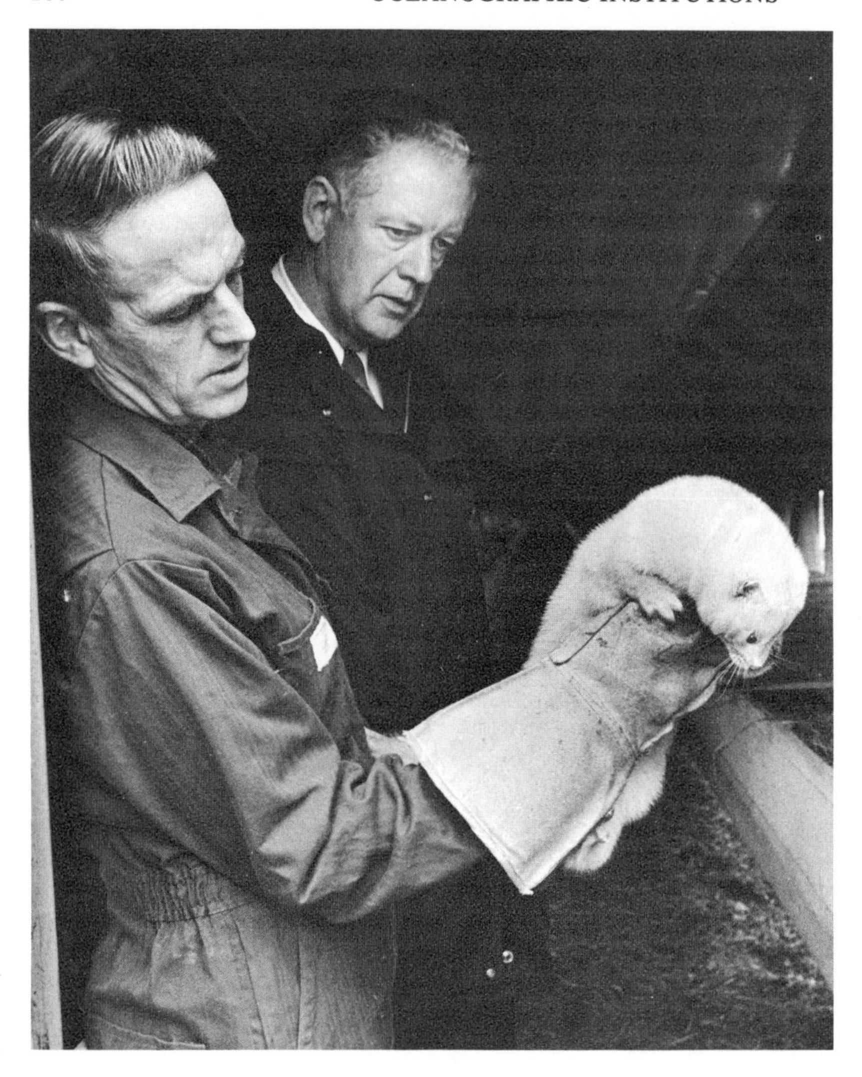

This healthy-looking mink has been fed on a diet containing 25 percent shrimp waste in an Oregon State Sea Grant project studying the use of seafood processing wastes as protein sources for domestic animals.
Oregon State Sea Grant College Program

tal upwelling zone. Studies are continuing on bottom-dwelling animals, both invertebrates and fishes, on the continental shelf, slope, and abyssal plain, and in selected estuaries. The daily vertical migrations of zooplankton (plankton animals) and micronekton (very small animals able to swim under their own power) are also being studied. These migrations take the organisms from depths of hundreds of feet up to the surface layers of the water and back down again. In addition, experimental research is continuing: on the ecology and physiology of phytoplankton; on the distribution patterns of zooplankton and on these animals' "life strategies" and grazing habits; and on the effects of pressure and temperature on deep-ocean bacteria. One of OSU's specialties is the study of the effects of pollution on plankton productivity.

The School of Oceanography also had a very active program in radioecology and radiochemistry. These fields are significant to Oregonians, since the Columbia River formerly carried radionuclides from the Hanford, Washington, Atomic Laboratories out to sea. The concentration of these radioactive wastes was low, but the flow was steady, and they provided an excellent opportunity to study the rates at which various sea plants and animals take up radioactivity. Using a specially designed gamma-ray probe the OSU researchers measured radioactivity directly on the ocean floor in the shallow water near shore. By chemically separating radioactive elements from seawater, they have detected radioactivity as far out at sea as 350 miles from the mouth of the Columbia. They have also found short-lived radioactive residues from atomic-bomb-test fallout in animals taken as deep as two miles.

The Marine Science Center at Newport houses a marine biology lab, a Pacific fisheries lab, and a public wing that contains an aquarium and museum. Scientists from OSU and other institutions use the marine biology lab for a variety of investigations: the effects of changing concentrations of oxygen and salt (which occur at every tide) on estuary-dwelling organisms, the feeding and growth of marine invertebrates, and the classification of sea animals. The fisheries lab studies the effects of pulp-mill wastes on marine animals, the culture of clams and oysters, fish parasites, population dynamics of finfish and shellfish, and related topics. A good deal of work is done in cooperation with the state Fish Commission laboratory, located at the center.

The central wing of the center, open daily to the public, performs a valuable public educational service. The 10,000-gallon aquarium contains local fishes and invertebrates. One of the most popular exhibits is the handling pool, which contains an assortment of such tide-pool denizens as starfish, sea anemones, sea urchins, sea cucumbers, and crabs that visitors are encouraged to pick up and examine. Another star attraction is an octopus living in an open tank near the entrance. Over 225,000 people a year visit the aquarium-museum, including school groups. Dioramas represent such marine-related subjects as coastal geology, tides, the marine resources of the state, and others.

Newport is also the base for the research vessels. The 177-foot *Wecoma,* new in 1974, is the ship for deep-water work. The *Wecoma* is also the ship on which the students get most of their sea experience. The 80-foot *Cayuse* is used mostly for coastal research, ranging as far as Alaska and the Gulf of California. Smaller vessels, including Dr. Burt's original runabout, are used for inshore and estuarine investigation.

One other activity of the School of Oceanography should be mentioned—the Latin American Program, whose goal is to assist Latin American countries to develop their own programs of oceanographic research and education. Students from a number of Latin-American nations are working at OSU; in fact, they form about 10 to 15 percent of the oceanographic student body. OSU also provides visiting experts to Latin American institutions, arranges exchange programs and cooperative-research programs, and trains technicians in certain specialties. One result of this program has been the development of a method of forecasting El Niño, a warm current that appears off the coasts of Peru and Ecuador about once every seven years, around Christmastime. The warm, nutrient-poor water displaces the normal cold, fertile water and plays havoc with the fish and seabird populations and the industries that depend on them. Predicting it is a great aid to government planners in Peru and Ecuador.

In terms of sheer size, the University of Washington is the marine-science giant of the Pacific Northwest. It boasts the world's largest and best-known college of fisheries, a renowned institute for marine studies, and a huge department of oceanography that grants undergraduate as well as graduate degrees—an educational rarity. At one point over 500 students were enrolled as oceanography majors.

An unusual specialty is American Indian fishing rights. This is an important issue in the state of Washington, with its large Indian population. Indian fishing rights are specified by treaty and sometimes conflict with the claims of non-Indian commercial and sport fishermen. Incidentally, the University of Washington Sea Grant program has helped Indian tribes establish their own aquaculture businesses.

The list of marine-science institutions could go on and on, but to describe them all would turn this book into a catalog the size of a big-city telephone directory. We shall therefore just mention a very few more. The Universities of Wisconsin and Michigan lead in studies of the Great Lakes, applying oceanographic methods to the biology, hydrodynamics, geology, and chemistry of these inland, freshwater seas. The University of Wisconsin also leads in undersea mining technology. The University of Alaska is strong in Arctic studies. The University of Hawaii is a leader in seismology, vulcanism, and tsunamis (tidal waves).

17

Government Agencies in Ocean Research

All around the world governments are heavily involved in ocean research. The United States is no exception. Some of this involvement is indirect, through grants and contracts with academic institutions. A good deal is done directly by government researchers on federal or state payrolls.

The largest government agency involved in oceanic research is NOAA (National Oceanic and Atmospheric Administration). NOAA was established in 1970 as a part of the Department of Commerce, combining functions that had previously been spread among several governmental departments. It manages eight organizations: the National Ocean Survey, the National Marine Fisheries Service, the National Weather Service, the Environmental Data Service, the National Environmental Satellite Service, the Environmental Research Laboratories, the Office of Sea Grant, and the Office of Coastal Zone Management. Between them, their activities range from the ocean floor to outer space.

More than 13,000 persons work at NOAA's network of stations and laboratories, about half in oceanography or an ocean-related field. (Because of the importance of oceans in forming our weather, for example, the Weather Service is involved in research on air-sea interactions. It also issues weather forecasts and storm warnings to ships, fishermen, and others whose work or recreation takes them out on the ocean or the Great Lakes.) NOAA also operates the nation's largest fleet of oceanographic research vessels, some thirty in all, ranging in length from 65 to 303 feet, plus a flotilla of small craft for inshore data gathering and updating nautical charts. Still more data come from four NOAA satellites orbiting the globe. For example, satellite cameras with infrared sensors can map the major warm and cold currents and their eddies. NOAA airplanes and balloons gather information on the atmosphere.

NOAA's main research arm is the Environmental Research Laboratories, with headquarters at Boulder, Colorado, and its water-related labs at Miami, Florida, Seattle, Washington, and Ann Arbor, Michigan. One of ERL's major programs is MESA, which sounds as if it had something to do with the desert country of the Southwest. It doesn't. Begun in 1973, MESA is an acronym of Marine Ecosystems Analysis Program, and a look at it may give a pretty good idea of the variety and scope of NOAA's oceanographic activities.

MESA has four major projects. The Program Office runs all the MESA projects and carries out research of its own. In 1975, for example, the director of the Program Office was one of a team that flew down to the southern tip of Chile to study a massive oil spill in the Strait of Magellan. This spill, even larger than the notorious *Torrey Canyon* spill off England, was caused by the wrecking of the tanker *Metula*. It failed to make the headlines only because it occurred in a distant, unpopulated part of the world. But by studying what happened to the spilled oil—how much evaporated, how much turned into tar balls, how much sank to the bottom—and what effects it had on sea plants and animals, the researchers could predict what was likely to happen in the event of a tanker wreck in the cold waters of the Gulf of Alaska. Such a disaster is almost certain to occur as tankers carry more and more Alaskan oil to the ports of the world. The Gulf of Alaska is stormy and frequently fogbound. And the end of the pipeline from the oil fields of the North Slope lies in an area prone to severe earthquakes. Later in the year, the Program Office sponsored an international conference of environmental scientists and managers to discuss the *Metula* oil spill. In 1976 plans called for further studies of the *Metula* spill, plus a worldwide study of hydrocarbon levels in the ocean and investigations of pollution from municipal sewage, agriculture, and industry in the coastal waters of Florida, and the estuaries of the Gulf of Mexico, San Francisco Bay, and the Great Lakes.

The largest MESA project is the New York Bight Project,

which covers the area from Long Island to Delaware as far out as the edge of the continental shelf. In certain localities, New York Bight contains the nation's most severely polluted salt water. NOAA scientists are studying water-circulation patterns and tides, the movement of sediments along the bottom, and the occurrence of poisonous substances in the water. They are also studying the rate at which organic matter (such as sewage wastes) in the bottom sediments decomposes, which affects the amount of oxygen available to living organisms in the water, and the incidence of bacteria in the water and sediment. The researchers have made the disturbing discovery that a number of strains of bacteria have grown resistant to antibiotics and to heavy metals. As yet they are not a threat to public health, but the implications are disquieting. NOAA is also studying plankton productivity in various parts of the Bight (as might be expected, plankton thrive better in the less polluted portions) and preparing baseline studies for the Environmental Protection Agency (EPA) on the dumping of sewage sludge.

The third MESA project is the Puget Sound Project, begun in 1975. Puget Sound, the great arm of the sea that juts into Washington State, is the planned terminus for tankers bringing Alaskan oil to the West Coast. This means a major oil port, with inevitable leakage as oil is pumped from ships to shoreside storage tanks. More refineries will be built to transform the crude oil into gasoline, fuel oil, and other commercial products, which will be shipped out again. Workers will move into the area to man the port and refineries; this in turn means that more sewage will flow into the sound. Therefore, to prevent Puget Sound from turning into another New York Bight, NOAA is undertaking a series of chemical, physical, and biological studies that should lead to a well-planned system of pollution control.

The final project is DOMES (Deep Ocean Mining Environmental Study), an attempt to determine the environmental effects of deep-ocean mining (say of manganese nodules on the floor of the Pacific) before mining actually starts. At first glance it might seem farfetched to worry about the side effects of grubbing up such a remote and inaccessible area of seafloor. But scientists and planners—and even some businessmen—have learned that the environment is like a gigantic and incredibly complex machine with millions of interconnected parts. Monkeying with any one of those parts could start a chain of wholly unforeseen and undesirable events. It is possible, for example, that sediment particles stirred up by the mining dredges could be carried to the surface by currents and interfere with the growth of phytoplankton (plant plankton), on which all other life in the ocean ultimately depends.

Manganese nodules carpet a patch of seafloor in the South Pacific, 17,000 feet down.

Lamont-Doherty Geological Observatory

To develop guidelines for designing and operating deep-sea mining equipment, NOAA is studying plant and animal plankton in the tropical Pacific, in a location where manganese nodules will probably be mined. It is also investigating water chemistry, circulation, and mixing in the upper portion of the water column, and working up computer models of the dirt plumes that the dredge heads and discharge pipes will spew out.

An ERL project that would have seemed futuristic only a few years ago is known as STORMFURY. Carried on by groups at one of the Miami laboratories, it is an attempt to reduce the force of hurricanes by seeding their clouds with rain-producing chemicals. In the course of this, NOAA has learned a great deal about the energy systems of hurricanes and the particular combinations of factors that produce them.

NOAA has many other programs besides these. One is coastal-zone management. Another is underwater exploration. NOAA's Manned Undersea Science and Technology office (MUS & T) works with submersibles, habitats, and life-support gear for divers. NOAA also works with the Navy on physiological studies to extend man's ability to work under water. NOAA's Office of Ocean Engineering tests and evaluates newly developed oceanographic instruments and seeks to develop better techniques for calibration. It also develops automated data-gathering buoys that radio information to shore. Some of these buoys have unconventional shapes, such as a disk or a boatlike hull. NOAA maintains a round-the-clock watch for tsunamis over the whole

Pacific basin and issues warnings for these destructive waves. And NOAA's marine environmental data banks at Washington, D.C., Asheville, North Carolina, and Boulder, Colorado, contain information from worldwide sources.

The National Marine Fisheries Service does research on commercially important and threatened marine animals, from such humble species as shellfish and menhaden all the way up to fur seals and whales. Its specialties include diseases and other causes of death in shellfish, and methods of identifying fish subpopulations (stocks of the same species that mingle in the sea but do not interbreed). One of the most-used of these methods is based on blood chemistry. Another specialty is research on estuaries, where most fishes spend a critical period of their early lives, and where the effects of pollution and destruction of the environment are most severe. NMFS researchers also study the ecological relationships of sea-dwelling animals with their environments. They investigate the behavior and survival rates of the Pacific salmon and other fish that must face the threats of dams and thermal pollution in the rivers they ascend in order to breed. On top of all this, they conduct population surveys and make predictions of the seasonal abundance of important species.

The National Marine Fisheries Service also has jurisdiction over the protection of marine mammals: whales, dolphins, seals and walruses, and sea otters. In addition to doing research on these animals and on the ecosystems that keep them alive, the NMFS has the job of enforcing protective regulations. One of its

Fish swarm around an experimental artificial reef constructed of concrete tetrapods normally used to fight beach erosion.

National Marine Fisheries Service

A National Marine Fisheries Service researcher found these white grunts patrolling the barnacle-overgrown wreckage of a German U-boat sunk during World War II.

National Marine Fisheries Service

National Marine Fisheries Service scientists gather photographic evidence of the colonization of an artificial reef of junked truck tires by marine life.

Richard B. Stone, National Marine Fisheries Service

major current efforts is to develop new gear and new fishing methods for catching tuna. The goal: to reduce the horrendous death toll of dolphins which are accidentally caught and drowned in the tuna men's huge purse seines.

One NOAA program is worth special mention—the National Sea Grant Program, established in 1966 by act of Congress. The goal of Sea Grant is to support research, education, and advisory services in marine science and engineering. By the end of 1976 there were almost 700 Sea Grant projects under way at over 150 universities in thirty-one states. State agencies and industries also received Sea Grant funds. Grantees are required to put up one dollar of matching funds for every two dollars of Sea Grant aid they receive. In 1976 Sea Grant awarded over $23 million.

Sea Grant projects are unusual in that they stress a systems approach in which every aspect of the problem must be investigated. For example, a research project to develop an aquaculture system for raising a new species of clam must first of all find the answers to the basic questions: What is the animal's reproductive cycle? What does it feed on? Can we develop a diet that will make it grow faster? Under what conditions of temperature and salinity does it grow best? But the researchers must then go on to work out the engineering of the aquaculture system. They must do an economic study to find whether the system will pay—the government does not want to encourage people to invest in projects that lose money for them. Other questions must be answered, too: Does the system break any federal, state, or local fish and game laws? Will it be a source of pollution? Does it meet state and federal food-processing regulations? What is the best way of marketing the final product? What is its social impact? No project is approved unless it is of demonstrable value, and economists, lawyers, social psychologists, and other nonmarine specialists may be involved in the project to make sure that it is.

A school that has turned in an outstanding performance in Sea Grant research, education, and advisory services for three years in a row may be designated a Sea Grant College. The first institutions to be so honored, in 1971, were the University of Washington, Oregon State University, Texas A & M University, and the University of Rhode Island. By 1975 these schools had been joined by the Universities of Wisconsin, Hawaii, Delaware, North Carolina, California at San Diego, the State University System of Florida, MIT, and a consortium of the State University of New York and Cornell. Making the grade as a Sea Grant College is more than an honor. When funds run low, the Sea Grant Colleges get priority.

Sea Grant also runs cooperative programs with the states to

help them assess and develop their marine resources, and it encourages the participation of private industry. An important aspect of the Sea Grant program is the marine advisory service (described in a later chapter). The original Sea Grant advisory service proved so effective that Sea Grant now runs the advisory services for all of NOAA.

Another government agency that has been deeply involved in ocean research is ONR, or the Office of Naval Research. ONR is a rather small body, but despite its size, it has had a major impact on oceanographic research in the United States since its founding in 1946. ONR is very active in funding research projects at academic institutions. Woods Hole Oceanographic Institution, Scripps Institution of Oceanography, and Lamont-Doherty Geological Observatory are three major oceanographic institutions that have been heavily dependent on ONR funds.

ONR was established in August 1946 to apply wartime research discoveries to peacetime uses. Even more importantly, it was designed to supply money for a broad range of scientific work to prevent the great war-born flowering of research from withering away. Its original mission was to support research of all kinds, but as other agencies like NSF have taken over large chunks of this task, ONR has turned its attention increasingly to matters of particular importance to the Navy.

Not all of these involve the sea. ONR sponsors research in theoretical physics, logistics, various branches of mathematics and computer science, engineering psychology, and so on. When it comes to oceanography, ONR covers the full range of research and adds a special field of its own—environmental acoustics, which is not only important for locating submarines but also for determining the structure of the oceanic crust and the water above it. In physical oceanography, ONR concentrates on the dynamics of various scales of motion in the deep ocean. In biology, the emphasis is on bioacoustics—that is, the noises made by fish, shrimp, whales, and other marine animals. Another specialized branch of investigation is "biodeterioration," which means the damage caused by boring and fouling organisms, fish that bite into electric cables, and so on. Dangerous animals like sharks and poisonous fish are another field of interest, as is bioluminescence.

ONR-supported programs have been extremely effective in developing our current knowledge of the world's oceans. It was ONR-funded research, for instance, that led to the exciting breakthroughs in seafloor spreading and the concept of plate tectonics.

Many ONR basic-research projects have paid off in commercial terms, such as techniques and instruments for offshore oil and gas exploration. The original surveys which led, as a by-product, to the mapping of extensive manganese-nodule deposits were supported to a large extent by ONR. ONR-funded wave-forecasting and ship-routing studies in the North Atlantic have saved millions of dollars in transit time and damage to ships. The famous research submersible *Alvin* was designed for ONR, which owns and leases it out for research projects where it is needed. A current ONR project is searching for potential sites for geothermal power plants.

Last but not least, ONR projects have turned out many Ph.D.'s who are now leading ocean scientists in universities, government, and industry.

The National Science Foundation (NSF), founded in 1950, is a major source of funds for oceanographic research. In 1975 the NSF requested $64.3 million for ocean research. (The total budget request was for nearly $800 million; so oceanography is only a minor item for the NSF. Still, $64.3 million is a lot of money.) In that year the NSF had seven major oceanographic programs, two of which were the international projects GARP (Global Atmospheric Research Program) and IDOE (International Decade of Ocean Exploration). The Oceanographic Scientific Support Program involved physical, geological, geophysical, and chemical oceanography. The Ocean Sediment Coring program provided funds for deep-sea drilling in the Atlantic and Mediterranean as part of the gigantic Deep Sea Drilling Program. Arctic and Antarctic research each had a program, the Arctic one to study the response of pack ice and the water beneath it to the forces exerted by the atmosphere, the Antarctic program for physical and biological investigations of the Antarctic continent and the seas around it, including the role of the Antarctic in generating weather. The Oceanographic Research and Facilities Program was designed to provide ships and other specialized facilities for research in the oceans, estuaries, and Great Lakes. Many of the newer R/Vs are owned by the NSF. It also promotes sharing of facilities through UNOLS.

The EPA (Environmental Protection Agency) is mainly an administrative agency, although it does conduct some research of its own. Where the ocean is concerned, the EPA's main interest is pollution, particularly that caused by oil spills. At Leonardo, New Jersey, the EPA has built a huge tank 667 feet long, 65 feet wide, and 8 feet deep for testing devices to keep spilled oil and other hazardous substances from spreading and to recover them from the water. The tank is equipped to generate waves two feet high and to simulate a towing speed of six knots.

For the most part, however, EPA contracts its investigations out to marine-science and oceanographic institutions. It also provides support for private industry's antipollution research. For example, the EPA has supported a project of the American Petroleum Institute that involved raising special microorganisms which could digest petroleum. The second step of the project was extracting substances from these organisms that could prevent oil from sticking to sand, rocks, etc., and wash away oil that had already fouled them. The third step, presumably, would be to produce these substances in large enough quantities to clean up a full-scale oil spill. The EPA also works together with NOAA on certain projects, such as the New York Bight Program of MESA.

EPA scientists and managers evaluate the results of the studies and take the appropriate action. Thus, in the case of New York Bight, EPA decided to phase out all dumping of wastes—sewage sludge, industrial wastes, and municipal garbage—by 1981. In the meantime, they ordered that sewage sludge be dumped at a new site where currents would carry it away from the shore.

The coastal states, including the Great Lakes states, have their own programs, mainly in fisheries biology and pollution control.

18

Oceanography in Other Countries

Although the United States probably leads the world in oceanographic research, there is plenty of activity in other countries as well. Japan is preeminent in mariculture. Aside from Japan, the nations most active in ocean research are in Europe.

A quick survey would reveal that France leads in such practical aspects as the use of tidal power and manned-submersible development, and is probably second only to Japan in mariculture. The Scandinavian countries lead in physical oceanography. Germany has active programs in all fields. Britain, with a long-established fisheries-research program, is now catching up in physical oceanography and expanding its research in chemical and geological oceanography. The Soviet Union is probably preeminent in Arctic studies, though apparently lagging in technology.

To do a complete coverage of Europe's oceanography establishment would take several books in itself; so once more we must let a few institutions give an impression of the rest.

Let us begin in the north, with Sweden, where I was able to visit some institutions personally. In the little west-coast community of Fiskebäckskil is Kristineberg's Marine Biological Station, the oldest marine-science institution in Sweden. Kristineberg is a small cluster of buildings located on a rocky shore a mile or so outside the village and close to the mouth of Gullmar Fjord, where so much of the original oceanographic research in Scandinavia was carried on.

It was in Gullmar Fjord, for example, that some of the first studies of internal waves were done. But Gullmar is best known for biological studies. Deep, and sheltered from the Skagerrak (an arm of the North Sea) by a sill at its mouth and a band of rugged granite islets, it is also practically tideless. The result is a well-marked stratification of its waters and an equally well-marked stratification of marine life. In the early days, some alert biologist noticed that water from different depths not only had different temperatures and salinities, but also had different kinds of plankton living in it. By looking at the plankton, an investigator could quickly tell which layer of water he was studying.

Kristineberg was a small fishing settlement when the first scientist began to go there on summer visits in the late 1830's. Intrigued by the rich variety of animal life, he trained two local fishermen to dredge up specimens for him. Within a few years other naturalists began to come to Kristineberg to do collecting, and an informal scientific summer community grew up, bringing a modest prosperity to the fishermen in whose houses they boarded.

In 1877 Kristineberg became a formal institution when the

Kristineberg's Marine Biological Station as it looked in 1892. The twin windmills pumped seawater for the aquarium tanks.

Kristineberg's Marinbiologiska Station

Royal Swedish Academy of Sciences bought the waterfront property of a sea captain named Bengtsson, complete with house, docks, boat sheds, and half a brewery, and turned it over to the scientists. From this unpretentious beginning, Kristineberg has grown into a leading scientific institution. For many years it was open only in summer; today it operates all year round, with a skeleton staff of resident scientists in winter and up to ninety visitors in summer. Purely a research institution, Kristineberg has no students of its own, but Swedish and foreign universities give advanced courses there in spring and fall. Researchers from the United States, Britain, Germany, France, Egypt, Finland, and many other countries have worked there.

Over the years the nature of the work has changed from the original descriptive natural history. The major emphasis now is on experimental biology, such as physiology and biochemistry, and population dynamics. The main experimental subjects are sea urchins, hagfish, and sculpins, all locally abundant.

These creatures serve science in some unexpected ways. The sculpins are used in diabetes research. By rendering them artificially diabetic, researchers can trace the parts played by zinc and other heavy metals in insulin production. And because the sculpin's insulin-producing glands are unusually large, they make excellent subjects for studies of comparative endocrinology. Experiments showed that fish insulin worked unusually well on human diabetes patients, with almost no side effects. As a result, researchers associated with Kristineberg are studying the structure of the insulin molecules of more primitive animals such as hagfish, lampreys, sharks, crabs, mussels, and starfish in the hope of designing a synthetic insulin for medical use.

Since the late 1930's a major portion of Kristineberg's research has involved sea urchins. These humble animals have contributed to our knowledge of developmental biology, biochemistry, embryology, and the transmission of nerve impulses. Regular shipments of one particular species are sent to a heart researcher in Stockholm.

Another long-term study has been that of the specialized small animals that live in the sand and clay of the bottom sediments. Only one millimeter or smaller in size, they play an unexpectedly significant role in the ecosystem.

Since the early 1960's Kristineberg has been involved in environmental protection. One of its earliest projects was to investigate the biological effects of the sulfite-laden waste from a paper mill at the head of Gullmar Fjord. Thanks in part to Kristineberg's findings, the offending mill switched to another process, the dying sea life began to recover, and—best of all from the government's viewpoint—the water stopped stinking and regained its former clarity, for a great part of the local income comes from summer visitors who come there to swim and sail.

Under the new director of the lab, Dr. Jarl-Ove Strömberg, the research has taken on new dimensions. One innovative program is a study of the effects of heavy-metal pollution on fish, crustaceans, and mollusks to see which of their body systems are most affected—nervous, digestive, circulatory, reproductive, and so on.

For the future, Dr. Strömberg, an alert, youthful man who speaks excellent English and has done research in the United States, envisions an expanded program of basic research to learn the reasons behind what he calls the recorded dynamics of benthic ecosystems. In other words, we already know a great deal about the organisms that live on (or in) the bottom—animals, plants, microorganisms—and we know what types of habitat they prefer. We know who eats whom. But we do not yet know why, nor do we know all of the interactions between these living organisms, the materials of the bottom, and the water. These are what Dr. Strömberg wants to discover.

He would also like to start a type of aquacultural system that he calls polyculture—in other words, a system that would include enough kinds of fish, crustaceans, plankton, and other organisms to form a miniature ecosystem. The system could be adapted to large tanks with a recycled water supply, and presumably the different plants and animals could utilize each other's wastes, somewhat on the order of Dr. Ryther's sewage-purification farm at Woods Hole, thus cutting down the need to add nutrients and to dispose of waste. Such a development, explained Dr. Strömberg, would be a boon to Sweden's fishermen. Under the new Law of the Sea, they would find their fishing grounds drastically reduced, since Sweden's territorial waters overlap with those of her neighbors. In some areas, if the territorial line is drawn down the middle, the Swedes will not be able to fish more than ten or twelve miles from their coasts.

Fisheries, however, are the province of the Institute of Marine Research, a state agency that lies a twenty-minute ferry ride across the fjord in nearby Lysekil. Indeed, Gullmar Fjord has an incipient research complex. In addition to Kristineberg and the Institute of Marine Research, there is a small marine biological station in Fiskebäckskil. Owned by the University of Uppsala, it operates in summer only. The IMR also operates a field station on the island of Bornö, farther up the fjord. Bornö is a center for hydrographic studies; scientists find the suspension bridge that links the high, steep-sided island to the mainland an excellent platform for studying the layering of the water and measuring internal waves as they surge slowly past. A photographic current meter, useful for such measurements, was developed at Bornö.

A couple of hours' drive south along the coast is Göteborg, Sweden's second-largest city and a thriving port and industrial community. Here, on a bluff near the harbor, lies the Oceanographic Institution of the University of Göteborg, which specializes in physical oceanography. In fact, it is the only school in Sweden where the basic and intermediate courses in this area are given.

The school can handle fifty to a hundred students. About ten of these are doing advanced work at any one time; the others are busy with the twenty-week-long prerequisite courses. Most of the graduates go to work for the state meteorological service or the regional environmental departments. Some go to Norwegian oceanographic institutions. But by no means all the students go all the way to an advanced degree. Many only want to acquire enough background in oceanography for a career in teaching, or to expand their professional skills.

Göteborg's Oceanographic Institution was founded in the 1930's with the help of large donations from philanthropic foundations and private citizens. One of its leading scientists was Börje Kullenberg, inventor of the original piston corer. And one of the institution's proudest features is a storage chamber where core samples are kept under refrigeration to preserve their original chemical and physical characteristics. Some of the cores date back to 1947–48, when the Swedish research vessel *Albatross* made a round-the-world cruise and brought back important geological evidence from the deep-sea floors. Incidentally, Kullenberg developed his corer at the field station on Bornö Island in Gullmar Fjord. The scientists of the Oceanographic Institution and those of the IMR work closely together. In fact, the IMR scientists use the Oceanographic Institution's laboratory facilities when they have difficult analyses to do.

The building also houses wave tanks, an electronic workshop where most of the institution's instruments are designed and built, and a plankton tower. Four stories high, this concrete shaft with glass observation ports at various levels stretches from basement to attic of the building. There are built-in refrigeration coils to give precise control of the water temperature so that observers can see how plankton growth increases or dwindles at various temperatures. However, the tower is no longer in use. Due to an architect's error, it turned out to be too heavy for its underpinnings when filled and had to be decommissioned when the building's foundations began to crack.

Another unusual laboratory feature is the electromeasuring room, shielded against outside electrical interference by a mesh of steel wire embedded in its wall, ceiling, and floor. In this chamber are done delicate measurements that depend on electrical conductivity, such as analyses of trace chemicals and tests of the radioactive content of seawater.

In Germany, the leading institution for oceanographic and marine research is the Institut für Meereskunde (Institute for Marine Science) of the University of Kiel. Located on the waterfront of the Kiel Fjord, the university's Institute for Marine Science has ten divisions that cover every aspect of ocean science except geology and geophysics. That is handled by the Geological-Paleontological and the Geophysical Institute, in another part of town.

Oceanography at Kiel goes back to 1870, when the first marine-research laboratory was founded there by the Prussian government. At that time Victor Hensen, who later coined the word "plankton," was already teaching there. In 1889 Hensen led the Plankton Expedition, which made the first quantitative investigation of the distribution of plankton in ocean waters. The research vessel steamed first to the tip of Greenland, then southwest to Bermuda, southeast to the tropical Atlantic beyond the equator, west to Brazil, then back to Kiel, with frequent stops all along the 15,000-mile course to collect plankton samples. To the astonishment of the scientific community, Hensen announced that his plankton hauls were far heavier in the chilly, foggy North Atlantic than in the warm, sunlit waters of the tropics. How could this be, when everyone knew that plants grew better the more sunlight and warmth they received? Many scientists devoted their efforts to proving Hensen a charlatan. Others, including Hensen's colleague at Kiel, Karl Brandt, probed further. Hensen had shown that light and warmth were not the determining factors for plankton growth—but what were they then?

Brandt fell back on the ideas of agricultural chemists and concluded that it was the amount of nutrients in the water that controlled the amount of plankton. After years of research by Brandt and others, it was learned that the northern waters are rich in nutrients (and plankton) because there winds and currents periodically bring up mineral-rich water from the deeper layers and mix it with the surface layers. In the tropics, there is little mixing, and the upper layers of the water, where plankton thrive, remain a biological desert. Incidentally, this lack of plankton is why tropical water is clear and blue.

After World War I, the center of German oceanography moved

to Berlin, and Kiel languished. In the 1930's new research facilities were reestablished in Kiel; the Institut für Meereskunde was founded in 1937. It was destroyed by air raids in World War II. After the war, with Berlin a divided city in the middle of Russian-controlled territory, it was obvious that no oceanographic research could be carried on there, and the Kiel Institute for Marine Science was rebuilt on the west side of Kiel Fjord. In 1972 it moved to a new, modern building. The institute is supported partly by the state of Schleswig-Holstein and partly by the German federal government. The institute has approximately 240 staff members, one third of whom are scientists, and about 100 students working toward the German equivalents of the master's and doctor's degrees.

Kiel continues to turn out valuable research on subjects ranging from the RNA in plankton organisms to deep-water anchoring systems, the use of computer models to analyze the bottom vegetation of the Baltic, and the analysis of floating tar in the eastern Atlantic. Major fields of research are pollution, marine nutrients, and air-sea interactions.

Kiel's scientists take part regularly in large-scale international projects, such as GARP, GATE, DSDP, CUEA (Coastal Upwelling Ecosystems Analysis), and IWEX (Internal Wave Experiment, which measured internal waves beneath the Sargasso Sea and studied their role in the energy budget of the ocean). They also do a great deal of work in the Baltic, on which Kiel is located.

Another leading German oceanographic institution is the German Hydrographic Institute in Hamburg, a government agency that belongs to the Transportation Department. A good deal of the Hydrographic Institute's work has to do with shipping. Some of its regular tasks are surveying and charting the German coastal waters and deep-sea lanes in the North Sea, issuing up-to-date maps and predicting dangerous wind and wave conditions and storm floods. With the aid of weather satellites, it also forecasts ice in the North Sea and the Baltic.

The Hydrographic Institute's chemists monitor radioactive and chemical pollution in German waters—they are the official agency for this watchdog task. Its geologists study the movement of sand along the seafloor as a special mission. West Germany's coasts are sandy, and storms and currents can easily shift the bottom around to create new and dangerous shoals.

Astronomers and geophysicists are a part of the hydrographic team. They prepare the official tide predictions, provide the national standard time signals, and do research on geomagnetism and gravity. Nautical engineers at the institute test compasses, radar, sonar, and other navigational instruments at sea. The hydrographers study the characteristics and movements of water masses. Data from all these investigations are used by oceanographers of all nations.

The Hydrographic Institute also operates a fleet of six research vessels. The pride of the fleet is the 271-foot *Meteor,* which is owned jointly with the German Research Association. This large vessel, equipped for every type of oceanographic research, has a 55-man crew and can accommodate as many as 24 scientists. On the after deck are a helicopter landing pad and a launching deck for balloons. Meteorological balloons that radio back data from the upper atmosphere are often used on *Meteor*'s cruises, and the ship contains a complete meteorological forecasting station. In fact, it is one of the government's five floating weather stations. The main winch holds 12,000 meters of cable, almost 7½ miles, and can reach the deepest known part of the ocean floor. There are fifteen labs, which can be modified for the requirements of each particular cruise mission. The big 2,000-horsepower diesel engine is mounted on a double vibration-damping system, and the ship has two bow thrusters that give it extreme maneuverability.

Among the projects in which the Hydrographic Institute's scientists and ships are involved are the effects of dumping wastes in the North Sea and the Baltic, JONSWAP (Joint North Sea Wave Project), North African upwelling study, measuring water movement through the North Sea by radioactive tracers (and also by direct measurements), and magnetic and gravimetric measurements in the ocean area around Iceland.

In Britain, one leading research center is the Institute of Oceanographic Sciences, a division of the National Environmental Research Council (NERC). The IOS was formed in 1973 as a merger of four existing institutions, which kept on operating as before, although under a new chain of command. Headquarters is at Wormley, a little town southwest of London and some twenty-five miles inland from the English Channel. The other branches are at Bidston, near Liverpool; at Taunton, an ancient market town (also inland) in the southwest of England; and at Barry, a big seaport in the south of Wales.

The work of the IOS is about one third biological and two thirds physical, chemical, and geological. Scientists at the Taunton branch specialize in studying the movement of sediment in Britain's coastal waters and in ocean engineering—that is, in developing better designs for piers, breakwaters, offshore drilling rigs, and the like. Bidston specializes in the physics of tides and surges and issues worldwide tide tables. Barry houses a central pool of marine scientific equipment that serves the IOS, other divisions of the NERC, and British universities. At Barry, too, are most of the vessels of the NERC research fleet. Wormley handles biological, chemical, and geological oceanography.

At Wormley there is also a group of scientists and engineers who work on instrumentation. One of their major developments was the Swallow float, invented at Wormley in the 1950's and named for its inventor, J. C. Swallow. The Swallow float is nothing more than a hollow aluminum tube equipped with a sonar transmitter and ballasted to float at a predetermined depth. Carried along by the deep currents, the floats broadcast their movements to surface vessels. It is fair to say that the Swallow float has revolutionized our knowledge of the current patterns of the deep ocean and our understanding of their connection with weather patterns.

Another Wormley contribution has been in the field of side-scanning sonar, which Wormley scientists have refined and improved. One of their masterpieces is a 32-foot-long, 7-ton device named Gloria, designed to be towed from a large surface vessel and map the deep sea floor. Gloria has an effective range of twelve miles and uses a narrow sonic beam that gives a sharp "picture" of bottom topography.

Still another technical breakthrough developed by the IOS is a "porer" for taking samples of water from *beneath* the surface of the mud and sand that carpets the ocean floor. Yet other projects include wave recorders, current meters, and digital processors for wave gauges. Built into the wave gauges, these digital processors will convert the wave measurements into computer code and beam them to the lab by way of a relay satellite. The result: a continuous record of wave heights that should give better understanding of the behavior of the sea.

The IOS owns no research vessels, but has the use of the National Environment Research Council's fleet. Much of its work is done aboard the R/V *Discovery,* which with its 3,000 tons of displacement ranks among the largest oceanographic vessels in the world. It was on a cruise of the *Discovery* that the first scientific studies of the mysterious holes in the floor of the Red Sea were made. Filled with scalding-hot, super-salty brine, these holes are evidence of the drifting apart of the crustal plates that hold the continents. Since the brine is extremely rich in metals, chemical oceanographers are studying it with great interest to learn more about the formation of ore beds in the sea.

The IOS also conducts studies of tides and waves. As part of this study it has developed computer models of the Irish Sea, the North Sea, the Bay of Fundy, and the Gulf of Maine. These models will eventually be used in forecasting sea conditions. The institution has even sent a team to Loch Ness, not to search for the fabled monster, but to study the internal currents, waves, temperature, and mixing of water masses in this sheltered semisea. Accessible even in winter, Loch Ness serves as a natural laboratory where all the dynamic processes of the sea can be studied in detail on a small scale. Another advantage, says the IOS, is that the salt-free waters of the loch do not corrode delicate instruments.

The IOS takes part in such international oceanographic projects as MODE, DSDP, JONSWAP, and JASIN, to name a few. JASIN (short for Joint Air-Sea Interaction Project) was the brainchild of IOS physical oceanographers who conceived it and did the initial planning.

Most of the IOS' marine biology research is done with animals living in the middle depths and on the bottom. A team at Wormley has developed ways of keeping deep-sea fishes and other animals alive in the lab long enough to experiment on their metabolism and reactions to stimuli. The IOS is also involved in studies of the world's dwindling population of whales, marking and tracking them and doing anatomical studies on dead stranded whales and some taken by commercial whalers. One aspect of these studies is compiling a record of the ages of whales at their death. This is done by counting the rings in the waxy ear plugs that all whales have. The younger the whale when it is slain, the fewer offspring it has a chance to produce, and this cuts down the number of future whales.

A long-term project is constructing a mathematical model of marine ecology—the numbers of different kinds of organisms in a given volume of water in a given part of the globe and their interrelated effects on each other. On the applied-research side, the IOS has been investigating a cold-water coral called *Lophelia prolifera,* which forms large, stony clumps that damage fishermen's nets. It is also working on improved methods of catching deep-sea fish, looking toward the day when the fish resources of the continental shelves run low.

Most fisheries work in Britain, however, is done by the Directorate of Fisheries Research, based at Lowestoft, on the east coast of England, and by the Marine Laboratory at Aberdeen, Scotland. Their main task is investigating the ecology and management of commercially important fish and shellfish species. One project that has received much attention is that of raising flatfish in cages in sea lochs and in tanks at power stations, where it is hoped that the warm outflow of water from the cooling systems will speed up their growth rate. Both labs are also working to breed fish that grow faster, utilize their food more efficiently, and can tolerate life within the cramped confines of a cage or tank.

Oceanography in France has a long history, dating back to the establishment of the first marine biological station in the 1830's. Today a chain of biological laboratories along the coasts of France carries on that tradition. These laboratories are operated by the Ministry of Education.

The Centre Océanologique de Bretagne is CNEXO's major installation. It houses seven major labs and the central data bank.

Mazo/CNEXO

The largest is at Roscoff, in Brittany, the peninsula that juts into the Atlantic at the northwest corner of France. Here some 700 students take courses in marine biology, marine ecology, and algology. (The last category includes all the algae from microscopic plankton organisms to giant kelp.) The 180 permanent researchers specialize in benthic fauna (bottom-dwelling animals), ecology, and tidal studies. Other notable biological stations

which divers have made simulated dives as deep as 1,600 feet. CNEXO hopes eventually to achieve live dives of more than 1,900 feet in the open ocean.

CNEXO's research fleet includes eight ships ranging in length from 105 to 246 feet. One is designed for work in cold waters; one is a mother ship for submersibles and underwater habitats; several are designed to double as experimental fishing vessels. An unusual "ship" is the manned research buoy *Borha II,* moored in the western Mediterranean in almost 8,000 feet of water in an area chosen for its high frequency of storms. The study of air-sea interactions is *Borha II*'s major mission (its predecessor was put out of commission by storm damage during such studies). The manned buoy's inhabitants also study physical oceanography and marine biology. *Borha I* was based on a plan proposed by Cousteau; *Borha II* is based on the same plan but was modified to make it more seaworthy.

One of the most distinguished oceanographic institutions in Europe is the Musée Océanographique in Monaco, nominally directed by Jacques-Yves Cousteau. However, in recent years Cousteau's time has been taken up with his own projects, and the work of running the museum is done by Commandant Jean Alinat, a French naval officer, physical oceanographer, and veteran diving companion of Cousteau.

The museum was founded in 1899 by Prince Albert I of Monaco. Its original purpose was threefold: to house the prince's vast collections; to be a center of marine scientific research; and

The massive stone facade of the Musée Océanographique rises abruptly from a seaside cliff.

Institut Océanographique

A giant squid shares ceiling space with full-sized fishing nets at the Musée Océanographique. At left is a group of stuffed fur seals shot by Prince Albert, an enthusiastic collector.

Photo Detaille

to educate the public. However, it was not opened to the public until 1910—the long delay was caused in part by the difficulty of constructing a building on the face of a seaside cliff and in part by endless disagreements among the board of directors on details of design. But even before its official opening it housed scientific congresses, a function it still fulfills today, and the laboratories and library were in use.

The Musée Océanographique today is a fascinating mixture of old and new. The basement holds a large, well-stocked aquarium, which is an immensely popular tourist attraction. Half of the ground floor is taken up by a huge, ornately decorated conference room that doubles as a theater for educational films on the ocean. (The films are beautifully planned and photographed by Cousteau and his associates.)

The other half is divided among a number of exhibits: skeletons of whales and seals taken by Prince Albert on his cruises, presided over by a melancholy stuffed polar bear; thousands of jars filled with preserved specimens of deep-sea creatures; and highly up-to-date educational exhibits. At the time of my visit, there were a magnificent collection of seashells from all parts of the world and a series of exhibits illustrating such topics as the anatomy and evolution of different types of sea animals, the uses of mollusks in medicine, physiology, and other scientific research, and the ways in which pollution spreads through the food chains of the sea all the way up to man.

The second floor holds more specimens—thousands of them—and models of fishing boats and fishing gear from every part of the world. There are scale models of Albert's yachts, a copy of the fish trap he invented, and a life-size diorama depicting scientists at work in the laboratory of Albert's last yacht. There are also a multitude of articles made from sea-animal products: tortoiseshell, coral, mother of pearl, and an ancient Phoenician garment woven of mussel silk.

This is the part of the museum that more than 800,000 visitors see every year. But there is another part the public never sees—the labs and the library. There are eight floors of fully equipped laboratories, for the museum was designed as a first-class research institute. Unfortunately the generous endowment left by Prince Albert to cover the costs of operation was eaten up by depressions, war, and inflation, and the museum can no longer afford to sponsor its own research. However, the labs are used by other institutions, among them the University of Nice. International agencies also use the museum's facilities. The International Atomic Agency has its marine-radioactivity lab there. One of its main tasks is standardizing methods of making very low-level measurements of radioactivity. With the aid of the United Nations Environment Program, it is extending its work to other sources of pollution, such as heavy metals and pesticides. The Scientific Center of Monaco is another user of the museum's laboratories. Its projects include these: using radioactive contamination in seawater to trace the movements of water masses; monitoring microbial pollution along the Mediterranean coast near Monaco; and radioactivity-dating ocean sediments both for oceanography and for archaeology.

Scientists from other countries occasionally use the labs for special projects. They also visit the museum to study its vast collection of zoological types and to consult the library. (A type specimen, to scientists, is the first one of its kind to be classified. It then serves as a standard of comparison for scientists to check their own specimens against.) The library contains some 12,000 technical works, collections of several thousand scientific periodicals, the complete reports of over one hundred oceanographic expeditions, including those of Prince Albert, and reprints of some 50,000 articles. It also issues maps and bulletins.

An adjunct of the museum is the Institut Océanographique in Paris, also founded by Prince Albert. This institution offers free courses in physiology of marine organisms, biological oceanography, and physical/geological oceanography to university students from all countries. It also has a full-time staff of scientific researchers. The institute each year presents a series of scientific seminars and popular-level lectures and conferences.

The money to run the museum and the institute comes almost

entirely from the admission fees paid by visitors. Neither receives regular government aid. And although Jacques-Yves Cousteau is the titular director of the Musée Oceanographique, none of the earnings of his films and books go to support it. They are used to support the independent oceanographic work he does with the R/V *Calypso*.

A quick look at the rest of the world shows varying degrees of activity in oceanographic research. Canada's leading academic institutions are at Dalhousie University in Nova Scotia and the University of British Columbia in Vancouver.

UBC's Institute of Oceanography was founded in 1949. Originally a research institution, it moved slowly into the field of training oceanographers. Until 1958 it had only five faculty members and had graduated only seventeen M.Sc. and Ph.D. students. In that year Canadians began to take a serious interest in oceanography, and the institute began its expansion. Today it has forty graduate students and seventeen faculty members.

Special areas of interest at UBC include air-sea interactions, which has led to UBC participation in such international experiments as BOMEX and GATE. One of their scientists has also studied the interaction of air and sea from an airplane. The study of internal waves is another major area. A new aspect of research is the possible role of internal waves in causing mixing in the upper layers of the sea, thus spreading pollutants more widely while reducing their concentration.

With so much of the coast of British Columbia taken up by fjords, the study of water circulation and mixing in fjords is a natural one for UBC. These studies have taken its physical oceanographers on cruises along the coasts of British Columbia and Alaska, and as far afield as Chile. As industry grows on the west coast of Canada, the question of how much waste can safely be discharged into the fjords and connecting coastal waters becomes a serious one. Studies so far show that although the deep waters are not stagnant, their circulation is so slow that they cannot accommodate large quantities of pollutants without the risk of a buildup to harmful levels. At the same time it has been found that the circulation patterns in the upper layers of the water are affected by the wind as well as by the water that flows into the fjords from rivers.

In biological oceanography, UBC marine scientists study the seaweeds of the Canadian Pacific coast. One aspect of this research is to learn how much seaweed can be harvested without disturbing the ecological balance of the coastal waters. Another special field of study is the red tide, which periodically infects the local shellfish and renders them poisonous. The eighteenth-century British explorer George Vancouver lost one of his men to red-tide poisoning in 1793, and the name of Poison Cove commemorates the fatal incident. UBC scientists hope to learn enough about the water conditions that produce the explosive blooms of red-tide algae to be able to predict outbreaks.

An unusual research specialty of UBC is marine fungi, with potential application to controlling or eradicating fungus diseases of fish and shellfish, fighting the marine fungi that rot wooden boats and piers, and possibly utilizing certain species to digest and break down spilled oil and other hydrocarbon pollutants in the water.

UBC also administers the international project known as CEPEX (Controlled Ecosystem Pollution Experiment). Irreverently known as the "big-bag project," CEPEX is designed to measure the effects of chronic low-level pollution on open-sea ecosystems. Two gigantic plastic bags, measuring some 33 feet across and 99 feet in depth, have been tethered in the protected Saanich Inlet on Vancouver Island. Supported by floats, they extend far enough above the surface so that the water inside the bags does not mix with the water outside them. Carefully controlled amounts of various pollutants are added to see their effects on plant and animal plankton organisms. The great size of the bags is intended to give as close an approximation of natural conditions as possible. Scientists from the United States, which funds the project, and from the United Kingdom are also participating in this ambitious experiment.

In the field of marine geology, UBC scientists are conducting extensive studies of marine sediments in the inshore regions, and studies of the Earth's crust in the continental shelf and slope regions within Canada's 200-mile economic zone are under way.

On the other side of Canada is Dalhousie University, in Halifax, Nova Scotia. Dalhousie has about forty-five graduate students in oceanography, with one faculty member for every four students. The Institute of Oceanography is relatively new, having been founded in 1959. Its most noteworthy research facility is a complex called the Aquatron, which was completed in 1971. The Aquatron contains a huge cylindrical aquarium fifty feet in diameter and thirteen feet deep. Animals can be introduced into this 184,000-gallon tank from a smaller holding tank, and their behavior can be observed through a series of glass viewports around the perimeter at various heights. The tank can also be used for testing oceanographic equipment. Perched on a rotating bridge above the tank, experimenters can tow current meters, plankton nets, and other devices at varying speeds.

There is also a tower tank, 35 feet deep, 12 feet in diameter, that simulates the upper portion of an oceanic water column. Special inlets and outlets permit experimenters to create three different water layers of different temperature or salinity. A high-pressure laboratory has a number of small vessels or chambers that can be pressurized to simulate conditions in the ocean depths. The largest, roughly the volume of a garden pail (eight inches in diameter and twenty inches deep), attains a pressure of 20,000 pounds to the square inch. The smaller ones can reach pressures of 30,000 psi. The pressure vessels are used to study the changes that take place in living organisms and in minerals under these extreme pressures.

The most heavily used facilities of the Aquatron are the ten controlled-environment seawater labs, where marine-biology researchers can vary the temperature and salinity of the water according to the needs of their experiments. In addition, the Aquatron keeps cultures of several species of plankton algae and animals.

Research projects at Dalhousie vary from those on a grand scale, such as the effects of ocean tides on the Earth's crust, to such narrowly focused ones as the proportion of food particles in bottom sediments devoured by one species of bristle worm, or the role of light in breaking down amino acids in seawater. Other typical projects: the possible function of a seal's whiskers in navigating and locating prey; the relationship among lobsters, sea urchins, and kelp beds; and tide-induced currents in the Bay of Fundy.

Across the harbor from Dalhousie is the Bedford Institute of Oceanography, Canada's largest marine institution and one of the larger ones in the world. Established in 1960, the BIO is a government institution and employs some 150 scientists and a support staff of 550. It is devoted entirely to research and has no educational programs. However, some of the Bedford Institute scientists are on the faculty of Dalhousie.

The Bedford Institute of Oceanography houses three separate laboratories that share services, staff, data, and equipment. This cooperation, remarkable in itself, is even more remarkable when one considers that they belong to two different government departments.*

Largest of the three laboratories is the Atlantic Oceanographic Laboratory, or AOL, which is concerned chiefly with physical,

* The AOL and MEL labs belong to the Department of Fisheries and the Environment; the AGC lab is part of the Department of Energy, Mines, and Resources.

This electric-powered, remote-controlled vehicle, developed by scientists at Canada's Bedford Institute of Oceanography, crawls along the seafloor taking readings and collecting samples. *Bedford Institute of Oceanography*

chemical, and geological oceanography. Its operating territory is the North Atlantic and the eastern Canadian Arctic waters. The scientists of the AOL measure the ocean and its dynamic processes, compile navigation charts and resource maps, and monitor water quality. They also have the mission of developing oceanographic instrumentation. Perhaps their outstanding achievement to date is the *Batfish,* a towed underwater instrument sled that "porpoises" up and down between the surface and any preset depth down to 1,300 feet, taking salinity-temperature-depth readings. A built-in tape device records the data for later playback. Newer models of *Batfish* feature an automatic bottom-avoidance device that steers them up and over rocks and rises in the bottom. Other data-gathering devices developed at the AOL include a hydraulic-powered drill for taking rock cores and an electric core drill that functions at depths as great as 1,180 feet. The electric corer has been used to retrieve rock cores from the taller peaks of the Mid-Atlantic Ridge.

Most fisheries research is handled by the Marine Ecology Laboratory, or MEL. The MEL is involved with fisheries research, biological oceanography, and environmental quality research. Typical investigations of the MEL include studies of the distribu-

Towed by a surface vessel, the Canadian-developed BATFISH instrument sled-planes between pre-set levels, taking readings.
Bedford Institute of Oceanography

tion of plankton patches, year-to-year fluctuations in primary productivity, and fish metabolism. One of the more specialized projects is an evaluation of the relationship between whales and seals—top-level predators—and the stocks of commercially important fish. This study involves not only calculating the biomass of fish and/or zooplankton that these large marine mammals must consume each year in order to survive, grow, and reproduce, but also the increase in numbers of fish that may be expected if the whale and seal populations are kept down by hunting, and the decrease in fish that may result if the whale and seal populations increase thanks to protection. A one-time opportunity for studying cetaceans at close range occurred in 1974, when three young blue whales were trapped by ice off the shore of Newfoundland. Before the ice broke up and liberated the trapped whales, BIO scientists were able to walk out to the whales and study their heartbeats, respiration rates, and echo-locating abilities.

The third lab is the Atlantic Geoscience Centre, or AGC, which is chiefly concerned with locating such seafloor mineral resources as petroleum and metal ores. Canada has a special stake in such investigations, because it has the second-largest area of continental shelf in the world, exceeded only by that of Russia. And as land resources dwindle, the continental shelves are fast becoming the next target for exploitation.

Canada's continental shelf is a prime area for oil and gas exploration. Sample rock cuttings and cores from every offshore well that is drilled in Canadian waters are sent to the AGC for analysis. About half of the Canadian shelf lies in the Arctic, which has spurred research by the BIO into techniques for dealing with ice and ice-infested water. (One experiment involved towing icebergs out of the way of offshore drill rigs and shipping lanes.)

The BIO does some work with submersibles for geological and biological observations. It also uses the little subs for under-the-ice work and to retrieve lost oceanographic equipment.

The major contribution of the Bedford Institute to marine science was the *Hudson*-70 voyage. This project sent the 297-foot CSS *Hudson,* queen of the Bedford research fleet, on an eleven-month voyage completely around North and South America, via the hazardous Drake Passage south of Cape Horn and home by way of the Arctic Ocean. In addition to mapping the ocean floor and collecting thousands of water samples, the scientists aboard the *Hudson* conducted such diverse investigations as plankton photosynthesis studies, studies of living organisms and water conditions in the fjords of Chile's far south, and collecting evidence of the scouring of the seafloor by ice masses in the Arctic. Ocean scientists from a number of Canadian and American institutions took part in various legs of the 55,000-mile voyage, and British, Brazilian, Argentinian, and Chilean contingents added to the international flavor.

Although only three working days were lost because of bad weather, the voyage had its tense moments. In the Chilean fjords, sudden, violent gusts of wind racing down from the surrounding mountains threatened to drive the ship aground, and in the Arctic it narrowly escaped being frozen in. In fact, the last leg of the Arctic passage was made with the aid of an icebreaker.

Some of *Hudson*-70's most valuable discoveries were made in the Beaufort Sea, a portion of the Arctic Ocean that borders on Alaska and the former Yukon Territory. Here, in addition to deep ice gouges in the seabed (bad news for offshore drilling and for ship movement), the geologists found submarine pingoes—gigantic frost heaves that are sometimes called ice volcanoes. Until 1970, when the voyage was made, pingoes had been known only on land. Seismic "pictures" of deep-buried sediments showed that ice scouring of the seabed began only a few thousand years ago. This suggests that during the height of the last Ice Age the Arctic Ocean was not ice-covered.

Other major programs at the Bedford Institute include a large-scale chemical and physical oceanographic study of the estuary and gulf of the St. Lawrence River, and a follow-up of a severe winter oil spill off Nova Scotia. One thing the researchers discovered early on was that none of the materials used to soak up the spilled oil would work after the oil had been floating around on the water for a few days. As a result, they had to invent new methods for containing the spilled oil under forbidding, near-Arctic conditions.

The Bedford Institute will undoubtedly make many more contributions to marine science as economic pressures bear more heavily on Canada's 117,000 miles of coastline.

19

The Training of an Oceanographer

How does a would-be oceanographer or marine scientist begin his or her training?

It would seem logical to begin in college by majoring in oceanography, marine biology, or a similar specialty. But every oceanographer, marine scientist, and student I spoke with warned me against this approach. It was imperative, they said, to begin by getting a firm background in one of the basic sciences: biology, chemistry, geology, or physics. Mathematics is also a useful background, owing to the increasingly mathematical nature of modern science.

There are colleges that offer an undergraduate major in oceanography. However, such courses are typically quite diffuse. They expose a student briefly to many branches of science, but not for long enough to gain mastery of any one of them. Students with a bachelor's degree in oceanography have found it difficult to get into graduate school or to find a job above the technician level. I met only one exception, an associate dean at a respected oceanographic institution. But this man may have been an exceptionally gifted scientist to begin with.

If the broad-spectrum approach to oceanography gives an inadequate preparation, what about the opposite tactic of specializing as an undergraduate? Here, too, there are dangers. A student who specializes too early, say in marine biology, sedimentology, or underwater acoustics, risks locking himself into a narrow specialty with little hope of advancement. In gaining a head start as a specialist, he has also deprived himself of valuable breadth and flexibility. The strategy that best meets the test of reality is to do one's undergraduate work in a broad-based traditional field of science and go on to specialize in graduate school.

Let's take our hypothetical student oceanographer as he or she leaves college, armed with a bachelor's degree and a good scholastic record. By this point in his career, he should have a general idea of which branch of oceanography or marine science he wants to get into—biological or physical, for example. He should also have done some research on graduate schools to learn which ones best fit his interests.

If possible, he will have visited several schools to get a firsthand impression of what they are like. The atmosphere of the school is important. Do the faculty and students have a good working relationship? Are the faculty interested in their students, or are they chiefly involved in their own research? Is their teaching load so heavy that they don't have enough time for conferences? Conferences between student and teacher are a vital part of the training of an oceanographer. The student not only gets help with his problem of the moment but also defines and sharpens his ideas.

The size of the institution may be important too. Some students do best in the close-knit environment of a small institution, where they can feel themselves a part of what is going on. Others prefer the stimulation of a large school, where there are more students and faculty to exchange ideas with. Oceanographic institutions, in fact, make a practice of exchanging instructors and researchers to bring in fresh viewpoints and keep from getting ingrown.

A student may shift fields more than once during his graduate studies. One whom I met took a B.S. in chemistry and an M.S. in general biology before zeroing in on marine biology for his doctorate. Another took his B.S. in marine transportation and served in the merchant marine for several years before deciding to go back to school. He then earned a master's degree in physical oceanography and a doctorate in civil engineering, and is now a marine advisory specialist. A third student, a woman, majored in sociology at college—a subject involving a great deal of statistical work—and went on to graduate work in the statistical aspects of marine ecosystems.

When the student is accepted by a graduate school, he is assigned to an adviser on the basis of his interests. Typically, he has a conference with the board of his department to assess his academic strengths and weaknesses. A prospective geological oceanographer or marine geologist, for example, might find that he is strong in seismology and mineralogy but weak on sedimentology. He might also find that his college math training is not enough to carry him through graduate work. After this evaluation, he would then be able to plan a course of studies that would compensate for the weak areas in his preparation.

Course work usually takes two and a half to three years for the master's degree and another year for the doctorate. Research, lab work, and preparing theses and dissertations may take up another two years. From the student's viewpoint, you use the first four years to learn techniques, make your mistakes, and get the course work out of the way. The last two years you do your productive research and work it up for your dissertation. Ninety percent of the research, one student told me, is drudgery—endless, repetitive observations and recording of data. But the satisfaction of coming up with an answer to a problem that no one else has tackled before makes up for it.

This student—to give an example of the kind of project one ends up working on—was doing his doctoral research on the feeding behavior of open-sea copepods. Copepods are tiny crustaceans, vaguely like a miniature shrimp, which sounds pretty inconsequential. But they are a major item in the food chain, and animals that feed on them have their own behavior controlled, at least in part, by the behavior of the copepods. So new knowledge about copepod behavior could potentially add to our understanding of other marine animals, including commercially valuable fish.

A student's day is long and hard. Many hours must be spent in the library studying reference texts and keeping up with the literature—that is, the reports of what is going on in his field of interest. A great deal of time must be spent in the laboratory, especially by biology students. A biologist must, on occasion, be prepared to stay in the lab around the clock to monitor his animals or plants. Physicists, chemists, and geologists, however, can usually turn off the lights at the end of the day and leave with a clear conscience, knowing that nothing is going to happen while they are gone.

One requirement—far from universally popular—is that every student must spend at least two weeks at sea on a research vessel. We have already mentioned the physical and psychological strains of an oceanographic cruise. But even if the students spend their whole professional lives at a desk working with data that others have gathered, it is necessary for them to have a firsthand acquaintance with the object of their study—the ocean.

A good percentage of marine scientists do not go to sea. One physical oceanography student I talked with, his course work now finished, spends his days in a basement cubicle feeding data into a computer. At the time we spoke, he was tracking deep currents in the western Atlantic by means of data from SOFAR floats set for a depth of about 6,600 feet. SOFAR stands for *so*und *f*ixing *a*nd *r*anging; as the floats drift along at their preset depth, they give out a steady beeping. Their beep signals are picked up by stationary hydrophones in Bermuda and the Caribbean islands and relayed to the lab by radio.

This student, whom we will call Sergio, is a Brazilian and plans to do his doctoral work on currents in the Bay of Santos. Santos is a major Brazilian seaport and industrial city, and the bay is now feeling the effects of industrial pollution, oil spills, and sewage. To handle these problems effectively, the current pattern must be mapped accurately. Otherwise pollutants might circle endlessly around in the bay instead of being dispersed.

United States marine-science institutions have a fair percentage of students from other countries. Sergio, with a master's degree in oceanography from a leading Brazilian university, came to the United States to complete his training because he could not get the courses he needed in his homeland. Perhaps because he has spent some time working as a government scientist between his studies, Sergio estimated that his doctoral research would take another two and a half years—about eight years in all.

This will make him about thirty-three years old when he finally receives his Ph.D. Most marine scientists get their degrees in their late twenties. A few, however, become interested in ocean science late in life and change careers. I have heard of one oceanographer who began his studies at the age of forty.

Many students go on to do a year or two of postdoctoral research, usually at a different institution from the one where they took the Ph.D. The purposes of the "postdoc" are various. One is to fill time productively while waiting for the right job to open up. Another is to increase one's professional competence. Not least important is the chance to make new contacts, since so much of the business of marine science is conducted on a personal level.

Despite the fact that the Ph.D. is practically a union card for professional recognition, there are some marine scientists who have been so busy doing science that they have never gone beyond the master's degree. These men and women have made very valuable contributions to scientific knowledge, but their lack of academic rank is usually a disadvantage when it comes to pay and prerogatives.

Since oceanographic and marine-science graduate study are

full-time occupations, students do not have outside jobs to pay for their tuition. Instead, the institutions use government funds to hire them as assistants. This arrangement gives the students the advantage of putting their academic training to immediate practical use as they do real work in their chosen profession. Some students teach undergraduate courses, which is good preparation for the time when they will be graduate faculty members training their own apprentice scientists.

Unfortunately, not all students make it through the grind of graduate study. A student may find after a couple of years that research is not really what he enjoys. Or he may learn that his doctoral research has led him down a dead-end path. (Presumably his faculty sponsor should have steered him away from this trap, but slipups do happen.) In theory, the unlucky student could start over again on another investigation, but few graduate students feel that they can afford that much more time out of their lives.

A frequent disaster is that a student will choose a dissertation topic that has already been staked out by a student at another institution. By the rules of the academic game, two dissertations on the same subject are not permitted. But fortunately students generally manage to find out through the grapevine who is working on what. So student A gets in touch with student B, and they work out a solution under which each will work on a different aspect of the problem.

It may sound as if the life of an oceanographic student is all drudgery and long hours. It is not. The students somehow manage to get some free time for their own interests. Since most marine-science institutions are on or near the water, swimming and sailing are popular. At Scripps, practically everyone grabs a surfboard at lunchtime. Many students and faculty members do scuba diving for sport.

Then there is more or less organized recreation. VIMS, for example, has dances and beer parties. At the Rosenstiel School there are regular poker games between faculty and students. There is even time for romance. I met a surprising percentage of oceanography students who had married fellow students, technicians, or administrative personnel.

Oceanography is a sociable branch of science, and oceanographers tend to be informal. One reporter observed that you can tell an oceanographer's rank by his clothes—the worse he dresses, the higher his rank. This may be exaggeration but I was told of one distinguished oceanographer who delivered an important paper at a scientific congress, dressed in a ragged sweatshirt and cut-off blue jeans.

What are the qualities an aspiring oceanographer needs? Intelligence, an inquiring mind, patience, and the ability to work hard are invaluable. An aptitude for science is vital. Graduate schools look for a good academic record, interesting job experience, and ability to communicate. An oceanographer's value to the scientific community depends very much on his ability to communicate his theories and his discoveries to others. The brilliant scholar whom no one can understand is not fulfilling his responsibilities. One of the most valuable qualities is the ability to set one's own directions, for in the end the student trains himself. Faculty, courses, and equipment are only aids to this goal.

20 The Outlook

Making predictions is always risky, and prophecies of what the future will bring for marine science and technology are especially risky because they depend so heavily on an unpredictable force—the United States Government. If the government decides to put a lot of money into marine research and development, there will be an increase in jobs on every level, and salaries will go up. If the government decides that it has better things to do with its money, then the job market will shrink. (The same holds true of every country that has a marine-science research program, for they are all dependent on government support.)

Oceanography has gone through this boom-and-bust cycle once before. During the boom times of the late 1950's and early 1960's money flowed freely into ocean exploration and related scientific research. Some came directly from the government, some by way of government contracts with private industrial firms. Ambitious experimental programs were planned. Ever more efficient research submersibles and undersea habitats were built. The future seemed limitless—until the country's resources were drained by the Vietnam War, and the ocean industry collapsed. Orders for equipment were canceled, and some of the smaller manufacturers went out of business. A number of highly trained experts had to find new jobs.

In fairness, it should be pointed out that the marine-science business is not the only one dependent on government largesse. Much the same thing happened in the space program, which was born in a national spasm of panic after the supposedly backward Russians lofted the world's first artificial satellite in 1957. By the early 1970's the United States had outperformed the Soviet Union in space feats, and the government's priorities shifted. The highly publicized man-in-space program was called off, with a few exceptions, such as the SKYLAB experiment. The unmanned exploration program was also cut back. With no private demand for moon landers and a very limited demand for communication and observation satellites, the result, again, was a shrunken market and scientists and engineers out of work.

Returning from outer space to the oceans, one gets a variety of opinions, depending on whom one asks. The public now and then sees an optimistic essay on the future of the marine sciences in newspapers and magazines. Yet professional journals such as the *Marine Technology Society Journal* present by no means such a rosy picture. And some of the scientists I spoke to were downright gloomy.

One of the leading optimists is Athelstan Spilhaus, one of the grand old men of American science. Spilhaus is also a distinguished educator and a prolific inventor and author. He envisions networks of floating cities that will supply most of their own food requirements by mariculture, perhaps fertilized by sewage from the mainland. He foresees offshore power plants that will generate electricity by utilizing the temperature differential between warm surface water and cold deep water, vast seafloor mining enterprises, whale ranching, and more. Less robustly optimistic scientists do not see these projects becoming a reality in the near future, and probably never on the scale Spilhaus envisions.

So, what does the future hold for young people who want to make a career in oceanography? Assuredly, very few of them will don scuba gear, flippers, and camera and swim off like shipmates of Cousteau. Scuba diving plays only a small part in marine research, and there is probably no one who can match Cousteau's talents as dramatist, poet, educator, and propagandist for the ocean.

Realistically viewed, the number of jobs for oceanographers and other marine scientists is limited. The oceanographic-marine-science community numbers an estimated two to three thousand men and women. Almost all of them work at academic institutions or government agencies. There is small prospect of expansion unless government policy changes again. Many oceanographers feel that the profession should not grow further, for fear that the quality of research would be harmed by an excessive number of scientists churning out trivia in a frantic scramble to justify their jobs.

At the time this is being written, the employment situation is best for marine geologists and geophysicists, since undersea exploration for petroleum is booming and seafloor mining may be about to take off. The fields of biological oceanography and marine biology in general are crowded. Physical and chemical oceanographers face less competition, though their fields are small, because of the highly specialized and abstract nature of their work.

The situation is somewhat better in ocean engineering. There is a need for men and women who can design robot observation submersibles, aquaculture systems, current-meter components, offshore drilling platforms, and ports for giant oil tankers, to name just a few of the tasks ocean engineers deal with.

But do young people who think they want a career in oceanography necessarily want to become research scientists or engineers? Judging from the mail received by oceanographic institutions, what "oceanography" really means to these young people is a chance to work with the sea in some way connected with science. And not everyone needs to be a researcher or a highly specialized engineer to work with the sea. The greatest need, whether in academic research, government, or industry, is for technicians.

A technician (at least in the marine-science world) is a semiprofessional with two to four years of college, or of college-level training. Technicians carry out most of the mechanical operations of sampling and lab work, freeing the scientists to think, plan, and evaluate their results. The following job descriptions (quoted from the Marine Technology Society pamphlet "The Oceans and You," 1973, which discussed positions on the research vessels of Scripps) give an idea of the different types of work that marine technicians are expected to be able to handle.

> Performs biological sampling from a research vessel; makes plankton hauls, records results, preserves and labels catch; observes, distinguishes, and records number and type of marine fishes, birds, and mammals; takes trawls at specified depths, preserves or maintains live biological specimens obtained; takes samples of water and bottom sediment for microbiological study, using specialized sampling equipment; makes measures of productivity; analyzes samples for chlorophyll and other organic constituents.

> Performs hydrographic station duties using Nansen bottles and other sampling devices; reads deep-sea reversing thermometers;

draws off water samples; makes and records bathythermograph observations on station and underway; makes a continuous temperature-salinity depth record; plots graphs and charts and prepares statistical summaries of data.

Performs chemical analysis of seawater for oxygen, salinity, phosphates, silicates, and other elements; operates equipment for continuous measurement of CO_2 content of air and seawater while underway; maintains shipboard chemical laboratory.

These job specifications are for seagoing technicians. Most technicians do not go to sea but perform the same types of analysis and computation in the relative comfort of a shoreside lab. For someone who is interested in marine science but does not wish to pursue an advanced degree, a technician's job may be the ideal solution. It might be worth adding that technicians sometimes earn more money than researchers.

Then there is mariculture, which can be expected to grow in importance as the world's population rises and the available resources shrink. A successful sea farmer needs intelligence and the ability to work hard, but he does not need an advanced degree. In some parts of the world there are highly successful mariculturists who have very limited formal education and got their knowledge on the job. Despite the optimistic predictions made in the 1960's, mariculture is not the answer to feeding the starving masses of an overpopulated Earth—there are limits to the amount of food a given volume of water can produce. But it is almost certain that mariculture will produce a large proportion of such "luxury" foods as oysters, shrimps, lobsters, and salmon.

A small but interesting marine-related profession is the operation of aquariums and museums. Curators and technicians of these institutions need a strong background in the marine sciences, particularly biology. Security guards, maintenance men, and administrative personnel do not. But they do not work with the animals, and there is no real difference between being a security guard, electrician, or secretary at an aquarium and doing the same job in a department store.

The list of ocean-related professions includes journalism, underwater photography, and underwater archaeology. A journalist who specializes in marine science may be a newspaper reporter who covers everything from oil spills to oceanographic expeditions and experiments like Project FAMOUS. Or he or she may contribute articles to magazines, or work on the staff of an ocean-interest magazine such as *Oceans* or *Sea Frontiers*. A number of journalists write releases for Sea Grant and similar government programs or serve as public-information officers at marine-science institutions. For this field of work a formal degree in science is not necessary—usually the journalist learns his or her science on the job.

Underwater photography requires artistic talent, technical skill, and a good deal of expensive equipment. It also requires thorough training in diving skills and safety procedures. Few underwater photographers achieve the reputation of a Doug Faulkner or a Ron Church, and probably few can make a full-time career out of it. But it can be a profitable sideline.

Underwater archaeology, again a limited field, requires a thorough knowledge of archaeological techniques as well as diving skills. The archaeologist must be able to recognize what he or she is looking at, how to photograph it in place, how to get it to the surface without damaging it, and how to preserve the object once it has been recovered from the seafloor.

An emerging profession is that of marine lawyer. Traditionally, marine lawyers dealt with such questions as territorial rights, salvage, and insurance. But now that governments are beginning to take an active interest in environmental protection, there is a growing need for lawyers to prosecute and defend those accused of polluting the environment. When the environment in question is the sea, as it so often is, the lawyers on both sides must have a good working knowledge of oceanography. Seafloor mineral rights and the Law of the Sea are other fields that call for lawyers with a background in ocean science.

Entirely new specialties may open up as man exploits the sea and its resources more intensively. There will almost certainly be a need for doctors who specialize in marine medicine: treating divers for the bends, nitrogen narcosis, and oxygen poisoning; treating victims of poisoning by jellyfish, coral, and venomous fishes; and taking care of other problems that do not occur on land.

As aquaculture expands, there will be a need for marine veterinarians to control disease on the watery "farms." Diseases spread much more rapidly in the water than on land, as mariculturists and aquarium owners have found to their sorrow.

A field that involves close contact with ocean science and with people is marine advisory service. Sea Grant advisers and others counsel commercial fishermen, sport fishermen, oyster farmers, marina operators, and people with beach-front houses. Their advice ranges from how to stabilize a sand dune to how to prepare a crab for market. Although it helps to have a marine-science background for this type of work, it is not absolutely necessary. There are plenty of slots for writers, photographers, and layout people that require no science background.

Marine education in the secondary and elementary schools is growing. School boards are becoming increasingly aware of the importance of giving young people an understanding of the sea. This creates a need for marine-education specialists to teach teachers, imparting a basic knowledge of marine science and helping them design curricula.

Even without government support, some expansion is bound to take place in the marine industries. Aquaculture already supplies half the nation's catfish and crawfish, nearly all the trout sold in restaurants, some 20 percent of our salmon, and a high percentage of our oysters. It will increase as the cost of fish caught at sea rises and most efficient technology brings down the cost of aquaculture. The fishing industry, too, will find better ways of utilizing fish and will exploit species of fish that are not used by man at present, such as the deep-dwelling bristlemouths and rattails. This is turn will create a need for seafood technologists and marketing experts.

For at least the last decade writers have discussed the mining of manganese nodules from the seafloor as if it were going to happen at any moment. So far, it has not. The technology has been there for some time, but the price has been wrong. There have been legal questions, too, as to who has the right to exploit the resources of the ocean floor beyond the zones claimed by coastal nations. However, as land-based ore deposits run low and prices rise, it becomes profitable to dredge ores from the abyssal plains 15,000 feet down, though the technical problems are formidable. Another valuable resource of the ocean floor is phosphorite, a mineral that can be used in farm fertilizers. And sand and gravel have been mined from the shallow waters of the continental shelves for more than half a century.

Not everyone can be another Cousteau, but the ocean holds plenty of jobs and endless fascination for anyone who is interested.

Glossary of Acronyms

AGC BIO's Atlantic Geoscience Centre

AIDJEX Arctic Ice Dynamics Joint Experiment

AOL BIO's Atlantic Oceanographic Laboratory

AOML NOAA's Atlantic Oceanographic and Meteorological Laboratory

ASDIC Anti-Submarine Detection Investigation Committee

BIO Bedford Institute of Oceanography (Canada)

BLM Bureau of Land Management

BOMEX Barbados Oceanographic and Meteorological Experiment

BT Bathythermograph

BUMP Boston University Marine Program

CEPEX Controlled Ecosystem Pollution Experiment

CLIMAP Climate Long Range Investigation, Mapping and Prediction

CMS College of Marine Studies, at the University of Delaware

COB CNEXO's Oceanological Center of Brittany

CNEXO National Center for the Exploitation of the Oceans (France)

CUEA Coastal Upwelling Ecosystems Analysis

DOMES Deep Ocean Mining Environmental Study

DSC Deep scattering layer

DSDP Deep-Sea Drilling Project

DUML Duke University Marine Laboratory

EPA Environmental Protection Agency

ERDA Energy Resources Development Administration

ERL NOAA's Environmental Research Laboratories

FAMOUS French-American Mid-Ocean Undersea Study

FGGE First GARP Global Experiment

FLIP Floating instrument platform

GARP Global Atmospheric Research Program

GATE GARP Atlantic Tropical Experiment

GEOSECS Geochemical Ocean Sections Study

GSO Graduate School of Oceanography, at the University of Rhode Island

ICES International Council for the Exploration of the Sea

IDOE International Decade of Ocean Exploration

IMR Institute of Marine Research, at Kristineberg's Marine Biology Station

IMS Institute of Marine Science, at the University of North Carolina

IOF International Oceanographic Foundation

IOS Institute of Oceanographic Sciences, a division of NERC

IPOD International Program of Ocean Drilling

IWC International Whaling Commission

IWEX Internal Wave Experiment

JASIN Joint Air-Sea Interaction Project

JOIDES Joint Institutions for Deep Earth Sampling

JONSWAP Joint North Sea Wave Project

LIAR Laboratory for Image Analysis and Research, a computer

MBL Marine Biological Laboratory

MEL BIO's Marine Ecology Laboratory

MERLE Marine Ecosystems Research Laboratory Experiment

MESA Marine Ecosystem Analysis Program

MODE Mid-Ocean Dynamics Experiment

MSRC Marine Sciences Research Center, at the Stony Brook campus of the State University of New York

MSX Multinucleated Spore of Unknown Nature

MUS & T NOAA's Manned Undersea Science and Technology Office

NACOA National Advisory Committee for Oceans and Atmosphere

NAS National Academy of Sciences

NASA National Aeronautics and Space Administration

NERC National Environmental Research Council (Great Britain)

NMFS NOAA's National Marine Fisheries Service

NOAA National Oceanic and Atmospheric Administration

NORPAX North Pacific Experiment

NSF National Science Foundation

OCS Outer Continental Shelf

ONR Office Of Naval Research

ORB Oceanographic research buoy

OSU Oregon State University

POLYGON A Soviet-conducted study of physical oceanography

POLYMODE A joint United States-Soviet Union investigation combining elements of the Russian POLYGON and the United States-sponsored MODE

RSMAS Rosenstiel School of Marine and Atmospheric Science

RUM Remote Underwater Manipulator, a remote-controlled underwater robot

R/V Research vessel

SCUBA Self-Contained Underwater Breathing Apparatus

SIO Scripps Institution of Oceanography

SONAR Sound Navigation Ranging

STD Salinity, temperature, and depth

TAMU Texas A & M University

UBC University of British Columbia

UNC University of North Carolina

UNOLS University-National Oceanographic Laboratory System

URI University of Rhode Island

USCD University of California at San Diego

VIMS Virginia Institute of Marine Science

WHOI Woods Hole Oceanographic Institute

XBT Expendable bathythermograph

Suggested Reading List

It is not practical to furnish a complete bibliography for this book, since much of my source material is in the form of personal conversation, interviews, letters, scientific papers, annual reports, catalogs, and institutional and government pamphlets. General readers may find the following selection of publications useful.

Bascom, Willard, *A Hole in the Bottom of the Sea*. Garden City, N.Y.: Doubleday & Company, Inc., 1961. An excellent presentation of geological oceanography and explanation of the ill-fated Mohole project by the man who is known as Father of the Mohole.

Behrman, Daniel, *The New World of the Oceans*. Boston: Little, Brown & Co., 1969. A chatty, informative overview of three leading oceanographic institutions, Scripps, Lamont–Doherty, and Woods Hole, and their work, marred by poor organization and excessive flippancy.

Ericsson, David B., and Wollin, Goesta, *The Ever-Changing Sea*. New York: Alfred A. Knopf, 1967. Well-written, clear account of all branches of oceanography by two Lamont–Doherty scientists.

Gaber, Norman H., *Your Future in Oceanography*. New York: Richards Rosen Press, Inc., 1967. A clear, straightforward presentation. May be outdated, but basically good.

Gordon, Bernard L., ed., *Man and the Sea*. Garden City, N.Y.: Natural History Press, 1970. An anthology of classic accounts of marine exploration, from the biblical story of Noah's flood to SEALAB II, aquaculture, and continental drift, compiled by an outstanding marine scientist.

Idyll, Clarence P., *Exploring the Ocean World*. Rev. ed. New York: Thomas Y. Crowell Co., 1972. An interesting, clear exposition of oceanographic investigation, usefully illustrated and topically arranged. Very good for historical background.

Raitt, Helen, and Moulton, Beatrice, *Scripps Institution of Oceanography*. Ward Ritchie Press, 1967. A detailed, sometimes tedious account of the renowned institution's first fifty years; one of the authors was the wife of a Scripps scientist.

Schlee, Susan. *The Edge of an Unfamiliar World*. New York: E. P. Dutton & Co., 1973. An excellent, authoritative history of oceanographic research in western Europe and the United States. One of the best general historical sources.

Teal, John and Mildred, *Life and Death of the Salt Marsh*. New York: Ballantine, 1974 (paperback). A clear, readable account of the interrelationships of the many life forms that inhabit a salt marsh, and of the processes that form and destroy the salt marshes. A sobering final chapter tells of man's destructive effects. As sources of food and nurseries for many marine animals, salt marshes play a very large role in coastal-zone ecosystems and are studied in every major specialty in oceanography.

———*The Sargasso Sea*. Boston: Little, Brown & Co., 1975. Very readable, firsthand account of a chief scientist's tasks in running an oceanographic expedition, plus lots of background on marine biology and hydrography. An excellent example of how oceanographic disciplines merge.

Vetter, Richard C., ed., *Oceanography: The Last Frontier*. New York: Basic Books, Inc., 1973. A very useful anthology of classic writings on oceanography, edited by the secretary of the Ocean Sciences Board of the National Academy of Sciences.

Wenk, Edward, Jr., *The Politics of the Ocean*. Seattle: University of Washington Press, 1972. A long and very detailed account of bureaucratic squabbling and competition for research funds by an ocean engineer who was involved in the melee through his position as science adviser to three Presidents.

Wertenbaker, William, *The Floor of the Sea*. Boston: Little, Brown & Co., 1974. A detailed, highly readable account of Maurice Ewing and the Lamont-Doherty Geological Observatory. Contains what is probably the best explanation of the discovery of the Mid-Atlantic Rift, and an excellent exposition of the theory of continental drift.

For readers who are considering the study of oceanography, the pamphlet *University Curricula in the Marine Sciences and Related Fields* is indispensable. It is published by the Interagency Committee on Marine Science and Engineering of the Federal Council for Science and Technology and can be obtained from the director, National Sea Grant Program, National Oceanic and Atmospheric Administration, 3300 Whitehaven St., N.W., Washington, D.C. 20235.

The following magazines are good sources of general information on oceanographic and marine-science topics: *Oceans,* published by the Oceanic Society, and *Sea Frontiers,* published by the International Oceanographic Foundation. More technical, but still understandable by the layman with an interest in ocean science, are *Oceanus,* published by the Woods Hole Oceanographic Institution, and the *Marine Technology Society Journal,* published by the Marine Technology Society.

Index